Higher Grade
CHEMISTRY

Higher Grade
CHEMISTRY

Eric Allan and John Harris

Hodder & Stoughton

LONDON SYDNEY AUCKLAND

CONTENTS

PREFACE

In writing this second edition, we have aimed to provide a concise coverage of the Scottish Certificate of Education Higher Grade course in Chemistry as set out in the 'Revised Arrangements' published in 1990. Each chapter deals with a separate unit of work, beginning with a summary of prerequisite knowledge. The text adheres to the order of units, and generally to the order of learning outcomes, as given in these arrangements. We decided that this was best for reference and revision but we appreciate that teachers may wish to use a different sequence.

The tinted sections within the text incorporate content which relates to non-fundamental learning outcomes. We have felt it necessary to give additional explanation in certain topics which would otherwise have been incomplete. Examples of this include the structure of benzene in unit 2, the use of Le Chatelier's Principle in unit 7, and reference to binding energy to explain nuclear stability in unit 8.

Although practical details are rarely included, the text frequently refers to appropriate experiments, usually illustrated by diagrams. Worked examples of numerical problems have been given and each chapter is concluded with a selection of examples for practice. The initials 'SEB' at the end of a problem indicate that the problem comes from a previous Higher Grade examination paper or from the specimen paper issued with the 'Revised Arrangements'. Parts of a question that test problem-solving skills are indicated thus: [PS]. Where this is given beside the total mark for a question, it is considered that the whole question involves problem-solving. It is assumed that students will have access to the 'Chemistry (Revised) – Higher Grade Data Booklet'.

We wish to acknowledge the helpful suggestions for improving the text made by a former colleague, Mrs J Cheyne, and the assistance in proof-reading given by our present colleagues, Mrs J Blaikie and Mr I McGonigal.

We are grateful to Mrs J Wallace for producing a substantial part of the original typescript. We also wish to thank the Scottish Examination Board for permission to print questions from past papers as well as the specimen paper.

E R A, J H H 1991

Controlling reaction rates

From previous work at Standard Grade you should know and understand the following:

a) A reaction can be speeded up by

decreasing the *particle size* of any solid reactant,
increasing the *concentration* of a reactant in solution,
increasing the *temperature* at which the reaction occurs.

b) *Catalysts* are substances which

speed up some reactions,
are not used up during reaction,
can be recovered chemically unchanged.

c) The concentration of a solution is expressed in moles per litre, i.e., mol 1^{-1}. You will also come across the alternative term *molarity*. A two molar or 2 M solution has a concentration of 2 mol 1^{-1}.

CONCENTRATION

As you are already aware, changing the concentration of a reactant alters the speed or rate at which the reaction occurs. We shall now consider the effect of concentration on the rate of a reaction in more detail.

A useful reaction to study in this connection is that between marble chips (calcium carbonate) and hydrochloric acid using the apparatus shown in figure 1.

As the reaction proceeds carbon dioxide gas is released and hence the mass of flask and contents decreases. A loose cotton wool 'plug' is used to prevent loss of acid spray during effervescence whilst allowing the gas to escape. The balanced equation is as follows:

$$CaCO_3(s) + 2\,HCl(aq) \rightarrow CaCl_2(aq) + CO_2(g) + H_2O(l)$$

Specimen results from an experiment in which 15 g of marble chips were added to 50 cm^3 4 M hydrochloric acid are given in table 1. The decrease in mass is the mass of carbon dioxide released and this quantity can be plotted

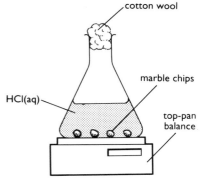

Figure 1

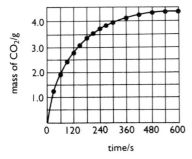

Figure 2 Mass of CO$_2$

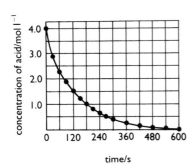

Figure 3 Concentration of acid against time

against time as shown in figure 2. From the loss in mass it is also possible to carry out a mole calculation involving the balanced equation (see Unit 3, page 71) to find the concentration of the acid at the various times. These calculated results are shown in the table and are plotted against time as illustrated in figure 3.

Time /s	Mass of flask and contents /g	Decrease in mass /g	Concentration of acid /mol l^{-1}
0	149.00	—	4.00
30	147.75	1.25	2.86
60	147.08	1.92	2.25
90	146.60	2.40	1.82
120	146.24	2.76	1.49
150	145.94	3.06	1.22
180	145.68	3.32	0.98
210	145.48	3.52	0.80
240	145.32	3.68	0.65
270	145.19	3.81	0.54
300	145.08	3.92	0.44
360	144.89	4.11	0.27
420	144.77	4.23	0.15
480	144.70	4.30	0.09
540	144.65	4.35	0.04
600	144.65	4.35	0.04

Table 1

The *rate of reaction* is the change in concentration of reactants or products in unit time.

As can be seen from figures 2 and 3, the slope of the graph is steepest at the beginning of the reaction and levels off as time passes. This shows that the rate of reaction is greatest initially and decreases with time. This is true whether we consider the rate at which gas is released or the rate at which acid is consumed.

It is difficult to measure the actual rate at any one instant, since the rate is always changing, but it is possible to calculate the *average rate* over a certain period of time. In this experiment the average rate would be calculated from the loss in mass or decrease in acid concentration which occurs in a certain time interval.

For example, the average rate of reaction in the first 30 seconds is calculated on the next page.

(i) In terms of the mass of carbon dioxide produced, the average rate

$$= \frac{\text{loss of mass}}{\text{time interval}} = \frac{1.25 \text{ g}}{30 \text{ s}} = 0.042 \text{ g s}^{-1}$$

(ii) In terms of the concentration of hydrochloric acid, the average rate

$$= \frac{\text{decrease in acid concentration}}{\text{time interval}}$$

$$= \frac{(4.00 - 2.86) \text{ mol l}^{-1}}{30 \text{ s}} = 0.038 \text{ mol l}^{-1} \text{ s}^{-1}$$

Carry out similar calculations for the next three 30 second time intervals and compare the results.

The relationship between the rate of a reaction and the concentration of a reactant can be more easily investigated using a different reaction. When dilute acid is added to sodium thiosulphate solution, the thiosulphate ions react gradually with the hydrogen ions to produce an opaque colloidal suspension of sulphur. The equation for the reaction, with spectator ions omitted, is as follows:

$$S_2O_3^{2-}(aq) + 2H^+(aq) \rightarrow SO_2(g) + S(s) + H_2O(l)$$
Thiosulphate
ions

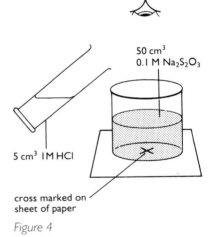

50 cm^3
0.1 M Na$_2$S$_2$O$_3$

5 cm^3 1M HCl

cross marked on
sheet of paper

Figure 4

Figure 4 shows one way of performing this experiment. After adding the acid, the reaction is observed from above the beaker. The mixture becomes more cloudy as time passes until eventually the cross on the paper is obscured. The time, t, taken for the reaction to reach this stage is measured. The experiment is repeated a few times using thiosulphate solutions at different dilutions. The total volume of thiosulphate solution and quantity of acid are kept constant. The cross is obscured when the same amount of sulphur has been formed.

Specimen results for this experiment are given in table 2 and shown in graphical form in figure 5. Since rate is inversely proportional to time, the reciprocal of time is taken to be a measure of the rate of the reaction.

The graph of rate against concentration shows a straight line. This means that the rate of this reaction is directly proportional to the concentration of thiosulphate ions. In other words, if the concentration of thiosulphate ions is

3

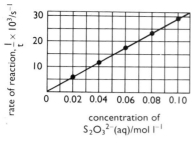

Figure 5 Rate of reaction against concentration of thiosulphate ions

doubled then the rate of reaction doubles. This relationship does not apply in all reactions.

Concentration of $S_2O_3^{2-}$ /mol l^{-1}	Time, t /s	Rate of reaction, $\frac{1}{t} \times 10^3$ /s$^{-1} \times 10^3$
0.10	34	29.4
0.08	43	23.3
0.06	58	17.2
0.04	88	11.4
0.02	165	6.1

Table 2

TEMPERATURE

The reaction between hydrochloric acid and sodium thiosulphate solution can also be used to study the effect of temperature on the rate of reaction. This time the concentration and volume of each reactant are kept constant, but the temperature at which the reaction occurs is varied.

Figure 6 shows how the temperature of acid and thiosulphate solution may be raised before transferring the beaker onto the sheet of paper marked with a cross. The acid is then added. The temperature should be measured at this point and at the end when the cross becomes obscured in order to find the average temperature at which the reaction has occurred. Again, the time, t, taken for the cross to be obscured must be measured.

Specimen results for this experiment are given in table 3 and shown in graphical form in figure 7.

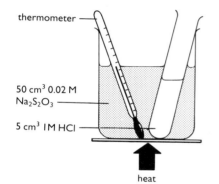

thermometer

50 cm^3 0.02 M Na$_2$S$_2$O$_3$

5 cm^3 1M HCl

heat

Figure 6

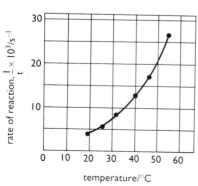

Figure 7 Rate of reaction against temperature

Average temperature /°C	Time, t /s	Rate of reaction, $\frac{1}{t} \times 10^3$ /s$^{-1} \times 10^3$
19.5	260	3.9
26.0	182	5.5
32.0	119	8.4
40.0	79	12.7
46.0	58	17.2
55.0	37	27.0

Table 3

As expected the rate of reaction increases with rising temperature. However, since the graph of rate against temperature is a curve, as can be seen from figure 7, the rate is not directly proportional to the temperature. In fact it can be seen from the graph that the rate of reaction doubles if there is a temperature rise of about 12°C.

There are many applications of the fact that a small change in temperature has a marked effect on the rate of a reaction. For example, roasting a chicken weighing 2 kg takes about 1 hour 30 mins in a hot oven (200°C) and twice as long in a moderate oven (150°C). If a slow-cooking pot is used, the cooking time increases to several hours, since the temperature is not much over 100°C. Food can be stored in a freezer for much longer than in a domestic fridge due to lower temperatures which slow down decomposition reactions.

Photographic film-developing is another example since careful control of temperatures is essential if good results are to be achieved.

$$2 \, SO_2(g) + O_2(g) \rightleftharpoons 2 \, SO_3(g)$$

The above equation shows the most important reaction occurring in the Contact Process during the manufacture of sulphuric acid. This reaction is carried out at 450°C in the presence of vanadium (V) oxide as a catalyst. Higher temperatures have a greater effect on the rate of the reverse reaction and thus the percentage yield of SO_3 decreases. Lower temperatures would increase the percentage yield of SO_3, but the reaction is too slow.

COLLISION THEORY

From an early stage in studying science, you will have been aware that all substances are made up of very small particles, which are called atoms, ions or molecules. Furthermore, these particles are continually moving, the speed and extent of the motion depends on whether the substance is a gas, a liquid, a solid or in solution. This description is often referred to as the 'kinetic model of matter'.

For a chemical reaction to occur, the reactants must be brought together in some way so that their particles will collide. This is the basis of the *collision theory*. Any factor which increases the number of collisions between the particles of the reactants per second is likely to increase the rate of reaction. More collisions occur if the particle size of a solid reactant is decreased, since its overall surface area is consequently increased. If the concentration of one or more reactants is increased, more collisions between particles will take place.

Raising the temperature at which the reaction occurs does more than merely increase the number of collisions between particles. Temperature can be regarded as a measure of the average kinetic energy of the particles in a substance. Hence, at a higher temperature the particles have greater kinetic energy and will collide with greater force.

Reactions occur, then, when reactant particles collide. However, it would appear that not all collisions result in a successful reaction. If they did, all reactions would be virtually instantaneous. Reactions in which covalent substances take part are often slow, even when the substances are gases as in the case of hydrogen and oxygen. This is because the bonds in the reactant molecules have to be broken before the new bonds in the product molecules can be formed, as shown in figure 8.

Unless ignited by a flame, a mixture of hydrogen and oxygen will not react to any appreciable extent at room temperature. This is despite the fact that, as gases, their molecules are separate and will mix rapidly by diffusion and many collisions between molecules will occur per second. As figure 8 shows, a rearrangement of bonds has to happen when the molecules collide if a reaction is to result.

Not all reactions involving covalent substances are slow. The colourless gas, nitrogen monoxide, combines rapidly with oxygen to form brown fumes of nitrogen dioxide.

$$2\,NO(g) + O_2(g) \rightarrow 2\,NO_2(g)$$

Reactions which involve separate ions in solution are often very fast if not instantaneous. When an acid and alkali are mixed, large numbers of the reacting particles, i.e. H^+ and OH^- ions, collide at the moment of mixing and rapidly combine to form water molecules. Similarly, mixing solutions of barium chloride and sodium sulphate brings large numbers of Ba^{2+} ions and SO_4^{2-} ions together and hence insoluble $BaSO_4$ is rapidly precipitated.

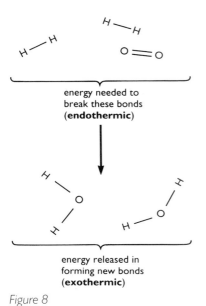

energy needed to break these bonds (**endothermic**)

energy released in forming new bonds (**exothermic**)

Figure 8

Ionic reactions involving a solid may be slow. For example, large marble chips react slowly with dilute acid at room temperature. As you are already aware, such reactions can be accelerated by decreasing the size of the marble chips or increasing the concentration of the acid or raising the temperature or, indeed, using any combination of these factors.

ACTIVATION ENERGY

In 1889 a Swedish chemist by the name of Arrhenius put forward the idea that for a reaction to occur the colliding particles must have a minimum amount of kinetic energy which is called the *activation energy*. The activation energy required varies from one reaction to another. If in a certain reaction the activation energy is high, only a few particles will have enough energy for collisions between them to be successful and hence the reaction will normally be slow. Conversely, a reaction with a low activation energy will be fast under normal conditions.

Chemical reactions often release energy when they take place. When an acid and alkali are mixed together quickly a temperature rise is observed, showing that neutralisation is an exothermic reaction. The combustion of fuels such as methane and petrol are highly exothermic reactions. During such reactions, energy possessed by the reactants (i.e. potential energy) is released to the surroundings and hence the products possess less energy.

Not all reactions are exothermic. In some reactions a decrease in temperature is observed as heat is absorbed from the surroundings. Such reactions are said to be endothermic. Energy is taken in and the products possess more energy than the reactants. The relationship between the potential energy and the path of the reaction, as it proceeds from reactants to products, is illustrated in figures 9 and 10.

The difference in energy between reactants and products is called the *enthalpy change*, symbol ΔH. We shall study this in more detail in unit 6.

Figures 9 and 10 can be extended to include the idea of activation energy, symbol E_A. This can be regarded as an 'energy barrier' which has to be overcome if the reactants

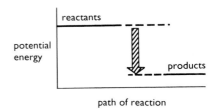

Figure 9 Exothermic reaction

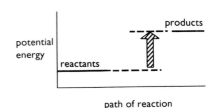

Figure 10 Endothermic reaction

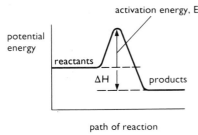

Figure 11 *Exothermic reaction*

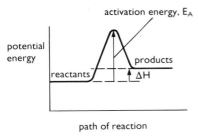

Figure 12 *Endothermic reaction*

are to change into products. This is illustrated in figures 11 and 12.

The greater the activation energy, the higher will be the energy barrier and the slower the reaction. The enthalpy change will have no effect initially on the rate of reaction. A reaction may be highly exothermic but it will take place slowly if it has a high activation energy. Reactions which illustrate this include:

(i)   the combustion of methane, which can be ignited by a spark,

(ii) reacting hydrogen and oxygen, ignited by a flame, and

(iii) reacting hydrogen and chlorine, which can be initiated by light, for example, by using a flashbulb.

Each of these reactions needs a supply of energy in some form or other to get it underway. This input of energy is necessary to increase the number of molecules with energy equal to or greater than the activation energy. In the first example, the heat released once the reaction has begun is more than enough to maintain the reaction. In the other two examples, mixtures of the gases react very rapidly once started and explosions usually result.

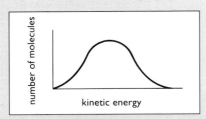

Figure 13 *Distribution of energy*

ENERGY DISTRIBUTION AND ACTIVATION ENERGY

At a given temperature the molecules of a gas have widely different energies. Most molecules will have energy near to the average value, but some will be well below average, while others will be well above. The distribution of energy values is illustrated in figure 13. You should be able to appreciate that the energy of individual molecules will continually change due to collisions with other molecules. However, the overall distribution of energies remains the same at constant temperature.

Figure 14 is essentially the same but incorporates the activation energy, E_A. The shaded area represents the number of molecules which have sufficient energy to react. A higher activation energy would mean a smaller shaded area.

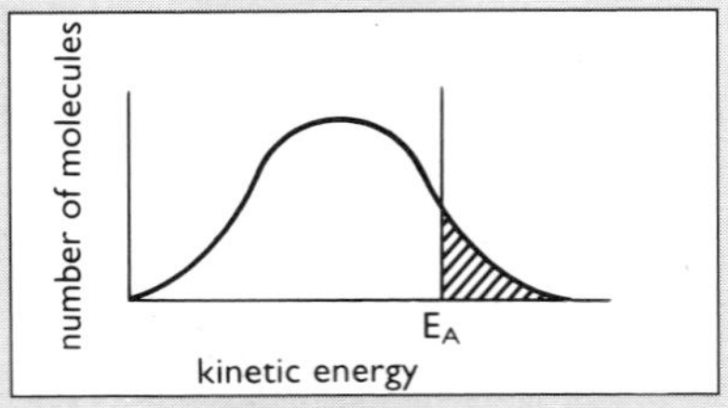

Figure 14 *Distribution of energy including activation energy*

The distribution of energies of a number of molecules changes when the temperature increases. Figure 15 shows that a small rise in temperature, from T_1 to T_2, does affect the average energy of the molecules. However, the most significant feature is the considerable increase in the area that is shaded. In other words, at a higher temperature there are many more molecules with energy equal to or greater than the activation energy.

This is the real reason why a small change in temperature can have such a marked effect on the rate of a reaction.

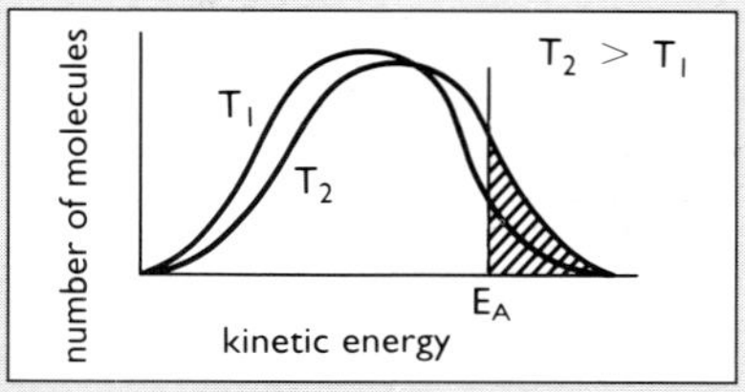

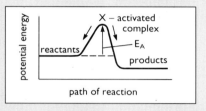

Figure 15   Distribution of energy at different temperatures

ACTIVATED COMPLEX

In going from reactants to products, an intermediate stage is reached at the top of the energy barrier at which a highly energetic species called an *activated complex* is formed. This is illustrated in figure 16 which also shows that the activation energy can be redefined as the energy needed by the colliding particles to form an activated complex.

Such particles are very unstable and exist for only a very short time. From the peak of the energy barrier the complex can lose energy in one of two ways and either yield the products or reform the reactants.

The addition reaction between ethene and bromine is believed to go via the activated complex shown in figure 17 when the reaction is carried out under certain conditions, namely, in the liquid phase and in the dark. The dotted lines in the structural formula of the complex imply an unstable arrangement of atoms linked by partial bonding.

Figure 17 also illustrates another important point about collisions between reactant particles, namely, that the *angle of collision* may be critical. In this example, the angle of collision shown in the diagram is most likely to lead to the formation of the activated complex. Molecules which collide at an angle very different from this may not form the complex even though they possess sufficient energy.

Figure 16

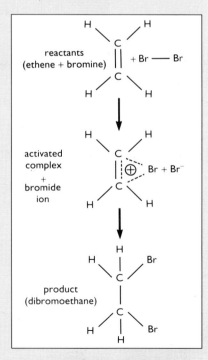

Figure 17   Reaction showing the formation of an activated complex

CATALYSIS

A *catalyst* is a substance which alters the rate of a reaction without being used up in the reaction. Most catalysts speed up reactions, but there are situations where substances called *inhibitors* are used to slow down reactions. Inhibitors are used, for example, in

(i)   rubber, as antioxidants
(ii) antifreeze, to combat corrosion
(iii) the plastics industry, to stabilise monomers during storage and transportation.

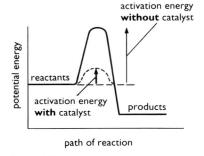

Figure 18

A catalyst operates by providing an alternative pathway for the reaction which requires much less energy on the part of the colliding particles. In other words, a catalyst *lowers the activation energy*. This is illustrated in figure 18 for an exothermic reaction.

A simple example of catalysis can be shown using hydrogen peroxide, H_2O_2. A solution of hydrogen peroxide evolves oxygen very slowly even on heating. Oxygen is much more rapidly evolved when manganese (IV) oxide is added, even in small amounts.

$$2 H_2O_2(aq) \rightarrow 2 H_2O(l) + O_2(g) \quad \text{Catalyst: } MnO_2(s)$$

Catalysts play an important part in many industrial processes, some of which you will have encountered in previous years. Table 4 summarises some of these processes.

Catalyst	Process	Reaction	Importance
Vanadium(V) oxide	Contact	$2SO_2 + O_2 \rightleftharpoons 2SO_3$	Manufacture of sulphuric acid
Iron	Haber	$N_2 + 3H_2 \rightleftharpoons 2NH_3$	Manufacture of ammonia
Platinum	Catalytic oxidation of ammonia	$4NH_3 + 5O_2 \rightleftharpoons 4NO + 6H_2O$	Manufacture of nitric acid
Nickel	Hydrogenation	Unsaturated oils $+ H_2$ $\rightarrow$ saturated fats	Manufacture of margarine
Aluminium silicate	Catalytic cracking	Breaking down long-chain hydrocarbon molecules	Manufacture of fuels and monomers for the plastics industry

Table 4

The catalysts listed in table 4, along with manganese (IV) oxide in the decomposition of hydrogen peroxide, are said to be *heterogeneous*, since they are in a different physical state from the reactants. For example, the Contact Process uses solid pellets of vanadium(V) oxide to catalyse the reaction between the gases sulphur dioxide and oxygen.

Although a catalyst is not used up during a reaction, it may undergo a temporary chemical change during its catalytic activity. This can be demonstrated by the reaction between aqueous solutions of Rochelle salt (potassium sodium tartrate) and hydrogen peroxide illustrated in figure 19. This is a slow reaction even when the mixture is hot, but it is catalysed when a pink-coloured solution containing cobalt (II) ions is added. The immediate colour change to green is possibly due to oxidation to form cobalt (III) ions which then catalyse the reaction. The return of the pink colour at the end of the reaction shows that cobalt (II) ions have been re-formed.

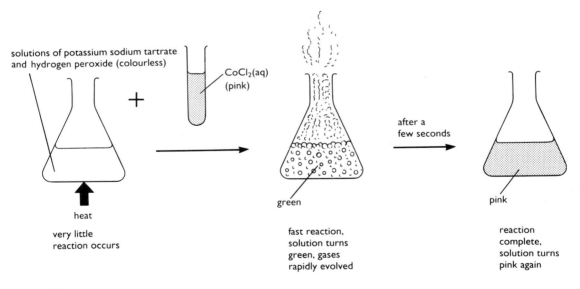

Figure 19

This reaction also illustrates the use of a *homogeneous* catalyst, since the catalyst and reactants are in the same physical state, i.e. in solution.

Most of the catalysts dealt with so far are either metals from the middle of the Periodic Table or are compounds of these metals. These metals are known as *transition elements* and catalytic behaviour is just one of their characteristic properties. Transition metals also have variable valency and tend to form coloured ions.

Many biochemical reactions in a living cell are catalysed by *enzymes*. Examples of enzymes include (i) amylase, which catalyses the hydrolysis of starch, and (ii) catalase, which catalyses the decomposition of hydrogen peroxide. Catalase is present in blood and helps to prevent build-up of hydrogen peroxide, a powerful oxidising agent, in the body.

An enzyme has a complex molecular structure and its molecular shape usually plays a vital role in its function as a catalyst. It operates most effectively at a certain optimum temperature and within a narrow pH range.

Enzymes are usually highly specific. Maltose and sucrose are disaccharides but are hydrolysed by different enzymes, the former by an enzyme called maltase, the latter by invertase. The hydrolysis of sucrose to form glucose and fructose is used commercially in the production of soft-centred chocolates and other confectionery.

$$C_{12}H_{22}O_{11} + H_2O \xrightarrow{\text{invertase}} C_6H_{12}O_6 + C_6H_{12}O_6$$
$$\text{sucrose} \qquad\qquad \text{glucose} \quad \text{fructose}$$

We shall come across enzymes again in unit 4, pages 90 and 91.

Certain substances may react with catalysts so that they operate less effectively or even not at all. Such substances are referred to as *catalyst poisons*. Traces of hydrogen sulphide as well as arsenic compounds should be removed from the reacting gases in the Contact Process before passing over the catalyst. Carbon monoxide is a catalyst poison in the Haber Process.

Catalytic converters should only be fitted to exhaust systems of cars which run on unleaded petrol, otherwise the lead compounds produced will poison the catalyst.

During the catalytic cracking of long-chain hydrocarbons carbon is a by-product and is deposited on the surface of the catalyst thus reducing its efficiency. In this case the catalyst can be regenerated by burning off the carbon in a plentiful supply of air. The spent catalyst is removed from the reactor and returned after regeneration.

HOW SURFACE CATALYSTS WORK

In a reaction where a heterogeneous catalyst is employed, it is usually an advantage if the catalyst has as large a surface area as possible. It is believed that catalysis occurs on the surface of the catalyst at certain points called *active sites*. At these sites molecules of at least one of the reactants are adsorbed. The function of a heterogeneous or surface catalyst can be represented in three stages as shown in figure 20.

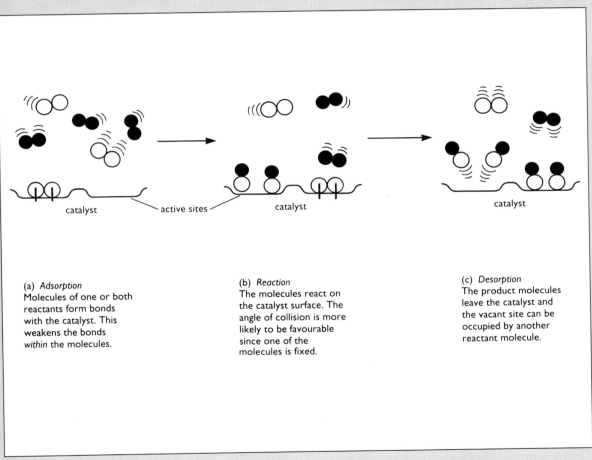

(a) *Adsorption*
Molecules of one or both reactants form bonds with the catalyst. This weakens the bonds *within* the molecules.

(b) *Reaction*
The molecules react on the catalyst surface. The angle of collision is more likely to be favourable since one of the molecules is fixed.

(c) *Desorption*
The product molecules leave the catalyst and the vacant site can be occupied by another reactant molecule.

Figure 20

This can also help us to understand how a catalyst can be poisoned. Poisoning will occur if certain molecules become preferentially adsorbed or, worse still, permanently attached to the surface of the catalyst. This will reduce the number of active sites available for the adsorption of reactant molecules and will render the catalyst ineffective.

Examples for practice

1. The graph shows how the volume of NO_2 released increases with time when 2 g of copper turnings react with excess concentrated nitric acid. Copy the graph (no graph paper required) and add corresponding graphs for the reaction between concentrated nitric acid and

(a) 1 g of copper powder and

(b) a 2 g piece of copper foil.

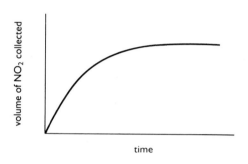

Label each graph clearly. Pay particular attention to the slope of the graph and the final volume of NO_2. (2)

2. Several experiments were carried out at room temperature with magnesium carbonate and acids. In each case, the same mass (excess) of carbonate was present at the start. The rate of mass loss was studied for various conditions as shown below.

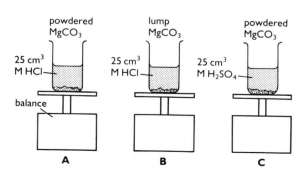

The results for experiment A were plotted on the following graph.

Copy the graph showing reaction A on to your answer book (no graph paper required). On the same set of axes, draw and label clearly the graphs which would be obtained for experiments B and C. (SEB) (2)

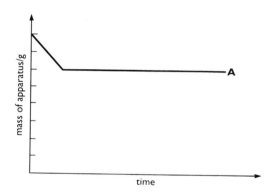

3. Excess zinc was added to 2 M sulphuric acid at room temperature, and the volume of hydrogen produced was plotted against time as shown.

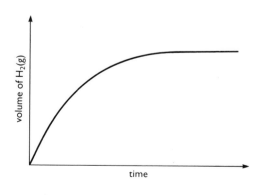

(a) Why does the gradient of the curve decrease as the reaction proceeds? (1)
(b) Copy the graph into your answer book (no graph paper required) and add the corresponding curves obtained when the reaction is repeated
(i) at a higher temperature;
(ii) using an equal volume of 1 M sulphuric acid instead of 2 M. (2)
(Label each curve carefully.) (SEB)(Total: 3)

4. The graph indicates an energy diagram for the decomposition of ethanal (acetaldehyde) vapour according to the equation:

$$CH_3CHO(g) \rightarrow CH_4(g) + CO(g)$$

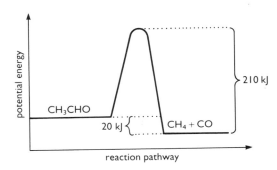

(a) What is the value for the activation energy of the reaction? [PS](1)
(b) What is the enthalpy change for the reaction? Is the reaction exothermic or endothermic? [PS](2)
(c) Iodine vapour catalyses the above reaction. Copy the above graph (no graph paper required) and on it indicate by means of a dotted line the reaction pathway for a catalysed reaction. (1)
(Total: 4)

5. $$2HI(g) \rightleftharpoons H_2(g) + I_2(g)$$

The reaction shown above is reversible.
The activation energy for the forward reaction is 183 kJ and for the reverse reaction is 157 kJ.

(a) On a sheet of graph paper show how the potential energy varies as the reaction proceeds. (2)
(b) From your graph deduce whether the forward reaction is exothermic or endothermic. (1)
(c) Gold and platinum both catalyse this reaction. For the forward reaction E_A using gold is 105 kJ, while E_A using platinum is 58 kJ.
(i) Using different dotted lines add this information to your graph. (2)
(ii) Which is the better catalyst for this reaction? Explain your choice. (2)
[PS](Total: 7)

6. The overall rate of a chemical reaction is often taken as the reciprocal of time (1/time). Graphs of rate of reaction against concentration and rate of reaction against temperature are shown.

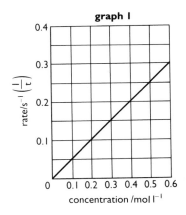

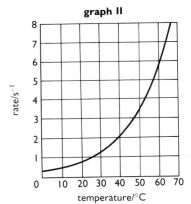

(a) From Graph I:
(i) Calculate the time taken for the reaction when the concentration is 0.4 mol l^{-1}. [PS](2)
(ii) Explain why the rate increases as the concentration increases. (1)
(b) From Graph II:
(i) Find the temperature rise required to double the rate of the reaction. [PS](1)
(ii) Explain why the rate increases very rapidly as the temperature increases. (1)
(SEB)(Total: 5)

7.

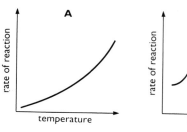

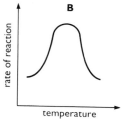

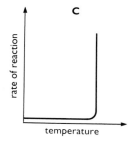

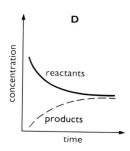

Which of the diagrams above could apply to each of the following reactions?

(i) $C_4H_{10}(g) + 6\frac{1}{2}O_2(g) \rightarrow 4CO_2(g) + 5H_2O(g)$

(ii) $CH_3COOH(l) + CH_3OH(l)$
$\rightleftharpoons CH_3COOCH_3(l) + H_2O(l)$

(iii) $S_2O_3{}^{2-}(aq) + 2H^+(aq)$
$\rightarrow H_2O(l) + SO_2(g) + S(s)$

(iv) $C_6H_{12}O_6(aq)$
$\xrightarrow{\text{zymase}} 2C_2H_5OH(l) + 2CO_2(g)$
(SEB)[PS](Total: 4)

8. In a class experiment it is found that 100 cm^3 of hydrogen gas are produced when 0.3 g of zinc react with excess dilute sulphuric acid.
(a) Draw a diagram of the assembled apparatus you would use in this experiment. (2)
(b) Pure zinc reacts slowly with dilute sulphuric acid. Adding a few drops of copper(II) sulphate solution produces the following results: the blue colour of the $Cu^{2+}(aq)$ ions fades rapidly, dark brown particles appear on the zinc and the production of hydrogen gas becomes rapid.
Using the apparatus you have assembled in (a), you are asked to compare the rates of reaction of:
Experiment 1: zinc + sulphuric acid, and
Experiment 2: zinc + sulphuric acid + a few drops of copper(II) sulphate solution.
You are further asked to plot your results in graphical form to show the difference in rate.
(i) Which of the species, $Cu^{2+}(aq)$ or $Cu(s)$, is likely to be acting as a catalyst? (1)
(ii) Give a reason for your choice in (i). (2)
(iii) State *four* conditions which must be kept the same in experiments 1 and 2. (2)
(iv) What do you measure during the course of the reactions which will enable you to compare reaction rates? (2)
(v) On the same set of labelled axes sketch the two graphs, labelled (1) and (2), which would result. (There is no need to use graph paper.) (2)
(SEB)[PS](Total: 11)

2 Feedstocks and fuels

From previous work you should *know* and *understand* the following.

a) How fossil fuels – coal, oil and natural gas – were formed.

b) How and why crude oil is separated into fractions by fractional distillation.

c) That molecular structure and physical properties of hydrocarbons are related.

d) The names, molecular and structural formulae of alkanes ($C_1 - C_8$), alkenes ($C_2 - C_6$) and cycloalkanes ($C_3 - C_6$).

e) How to identify isomers and draw their structural formulae.

f) What is meant by saturated and unsaturated carbon compounds and how they can be distinguished.

g) What happens during addition reactions and cracking.

h) That polymerisation occurs by addition or condensation and be able to show how monomer molecules interact in these two processes.

i) That ethanol is an alkanol and can be made from glucose by fermentation.

j) How a catalyst functions (Unit 1, page 13).

FEEDSTOCK OR FUEL?

You should already be familiar with the idea that coal, oil and natural gas are finite resources and are not readily renewable. They contain many carbon compounds which may be useful either as fuels or as feedstocks. A feedstock is a substance from which other chemicals can be extracted or produced.

Consequently there are likely to be competing demands for a particular substance to be used as a fuel or as a feedstock. Ethane, a constituent of natural gas, may act as a fuel when burned along with methane or it may be extracted and used as a feedstock by converting it to ethene for making plastics. The gasoline/naphtha fraction obtained from crude oil may be further refined to give petrol, a very important fuel, or may be processed in a different way to yield the starting materials for making nylon. Whether a certain carbon compound or mixture of compounds is used as a feedstock or fuel will depend on consumer demand at the time.

TEXTILES e.g.	PLASTICS e.g.	DYES e.g.
(a) *Acrylic* $CN \quad CN \quad CN$ $— CH_2CHCH_2CHCH_2CH —$ (b) *Polyester* $+OC_2H_4OC—\bigcirc—C+_n$ (c) *Nylon* $+NHC_6H_{12}NHCOC_4H_8CO+_n$	(a) *PVC* $Cl \quad Cl \quad Cl$ $— CH_2CHCH_2CHCH_2CH —$ (b) *Polypropene* $CH_3 \quad CH_3 \quad CH_3$ $— CH_2CHCH_2CHCH_2CH —$ (c) *Polystyrene* $— CH_2CHCH_2CHCH_2CH —$	(a) *Indigo (for blue denim)* (b) *Azodyes e.g. 'Para red'* (c) *Anthraquinone dyes e.g.*
AGRICULTURAL CHEMICALS	DETERGENTS These contain	COSMETICS
(a) *Herbicides e.g. '2,4 – D'* $Cl—\bigcirc—OCH_2COOH$ Cl (b) *Pesticides e.g. 'Malathion'* $(CH_3O)_2PS_2CHCO_2C_2H_5$ $CH_2CO_2C_2H_5$	(a) *Anionic surfactants e.g.* $C_{12}H_{25}—\bigcirc—SO_3^-Na^+$ (b) *Non–ionic surfactants e.g.* $C_8H_{17}—\bigcirc—O+C_2H_4O+_{13}H$	(a) *Perfumes may include ethyl vanillin:* $HO—\bigcirc—CHO$ C_2H_5 (b) *Lipsticks include coloured compounds e.g.*

Table I

Table 1 gives several examples of carbon compounds which occur in a variety of consumer products. The formulae show their complex molecular structure and need not be memorised. These compounds are manufactured by synthesis (or 'building up') through combining together small reactive molecules.

HOMOLOGOUS SERIES AND FUNCTIONAL GROUPS

You have already come across two important series of hydrocarbons called the *alkanes* and *alkenes*. Names and molecular formulae of members with up to eight carbon atoms per molecule are listed below as well as structural formulae of the first few members, see table 2.

Alkanes		Alkenes	
Methane CH_4	H—C—H (with H above and below C)		
Ethane C_2H_6	H—C—C—H (with H's above and below each C)	Ethene C_2H_4	C=C (with H's on each side)
Propane C_3H_8	H—C—C—C—H (with H's above and below each C)	Propene C_3H_6	H—C—C=C (with H's)
Butane C_4H_{10}		Butene C_4H_8	
Pentane C_5H_{12}		Pentene C_5H_{10}	
Hexane C_6H_{14}		Hexene C_6H_{12}	
Heptane C_7H_{16}		Heptene C_7H_{14}	
Octane C_8H_{18}		Octene C_8H_{16}	
General formula: C_nH_{2n+2}		General formula: C_nH_{2n}	

Table 2

Each of these series is an example of an *homologous series*. Members of a given series, known as *homologues*, have the following characteristics:

a) Physical properties show a gradual change from one member to the next.
b) Chemical properties and methods of preparation are very similar.
c) Successive members differ in formula by $-CH_2-$ and as a result molecular masses differ by 14.
d) They can be represented by a *general formula*.
e) Members of a series possess the same *functional group*, i.e. a certain group of atoms which is mainly responsible for the characteristic chemical properties of that homologous series.

Alkanes are *saturated* hydrocarbons since they have only single bonds between carbon atoms and as a result contain the maximum number of hydrogen atoms.

propene + bromine

$$H-\underset{\underset{H}{|}}{\overset{\overset{H}{|}}{C}}-\underset{\underset{H}{|}}{\overset{\overset{H}{|}}{C}}=C\overset{H}{\underset{H}{\diagdown}} \quad + \quad Br-Br$$

↓

$$H-\underset{\underset{H}{|}}{\overset{\overset{H}{|}}{C}}-\underset{\underset{Br}{|}}{\overset{\overset{H}{|}}{C}}-\underset{\underset{Br}{|}}{\overset{\overset{H}{|}}{C}}-H$$

1, 2–dibromopropane

Alkenes contain a carbon–carbon double bond (C = C) and hence are *unsaturated*. This can be shown by rapid decoloration of bromine water when mixed with an alkene, such as propene (see left).

This is an *addition* reaction which shows the presence of the C = C bond in propene. The carbon–carbon double bond is an example of a functional group since it is responsible for the characteristic reactivity of alkenes.

Three more homologous series are shown in table 3. Each series has its distinctive functional group. Names and formulae of the first three members are also given.

Name of series	Alkanols	Alkanoic acids	Amines
Functional group	—OH (hydroxyl group)	—COOH (carboxyl group)	—NH$_2$ (amino group)
First three members	Methanol CH_3OH	Methanoic acid $HCOOH$	Methylamine CH_3NH_2
	Ethanol CH_3CH_2OH	Ethanoic acid CH_3COOH	Ethylamine $CH_3CH_2NH_2$
	Propanol $CH_3CH_2CH_2OH$	Propanoic acid CH_3CH_2COOH	Propylamine $CH_3CH_2CH_2NH_2$

Table 3

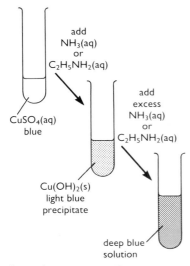

add NH$_3$(aq) or C$_2$H$_5$NH$_2$(aq)

CuSO$_4$(aq) blue

Cu(OH)$_2$(s) light blue precipitate

add excess NH$_3$(aq) or C$_2$H$_5$NH$_2$(aq)

deep blue solution

Figure 1

Alkanoic acids are not the only compounds to contain a carboxyl group. The –COOH group is also found in unsaturated acids and aromatic acids. Compounds which contain this group are more generally known as *carboxylic acids*. Similarly carbon compounds which contain the hydroxyl group are more generally known as *alcohols*.

It is interesting to compare and contrast the properties of members of different series e.g. ethanol and ethanoic acid, as illustrated in table 4 on the next page.

Amines show certain similarities to ammonia. For example, aqueous solutions of ethylamine and ammonia are alkaline and both form a deep-blue solution with copper(II) sulphate solution, as shown in figure 1.

These simple tests illustrate the point made earlier that the chemical behaviour of members of an homologous series depends on the functional group present. Members

Test	Ethanol	Ethanoic acid
Flammability	Flammable CO_2 and H_2O formed	Flammable CO_2 and H_2O formed
Addition to water	Miscible	Miscible
pH of aqueous solution	pH 7 i.e. neutral	pH <7 (around 3) i.e. weak acid
Addition of Mg to aqueous solution	No reaction	Mg dissolves, H_2 gas evolved

Table 4

of different series may react together usually by interaction of their functional groups.

The following word equations describe *condensation* reactions in which organic molecules combine with the removal of water.

Alkanol + Alkanoic Acid → Ester + Water

Amine + Alkanoic Acic → Amide + Water

The formation of esters will be dealt with in unit 4, see page 83. The formation of an *amide* can be illustrated as follows. Note how the functional groups interact.

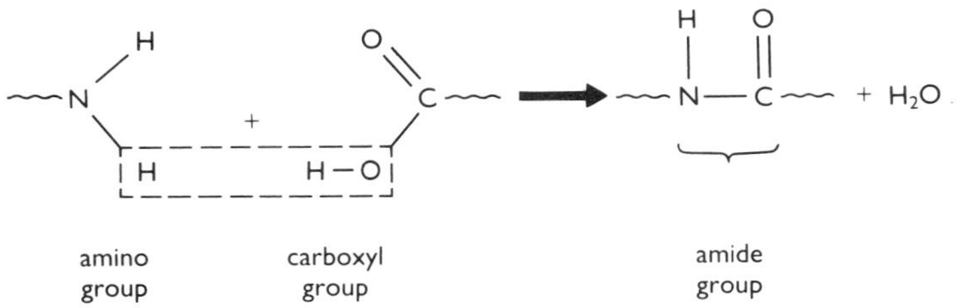

amino group   carboxyl group   amide group

Nylon is a *polyamide*, synthesised by condensation of two monomers. One is called a *diamine* since it has two amino groups; the other, which has two carboxyl groups, is called a *diacid*.

The structure of nylon resulting from the condensation of two diamine molecules and two diacid molecules is shown below.

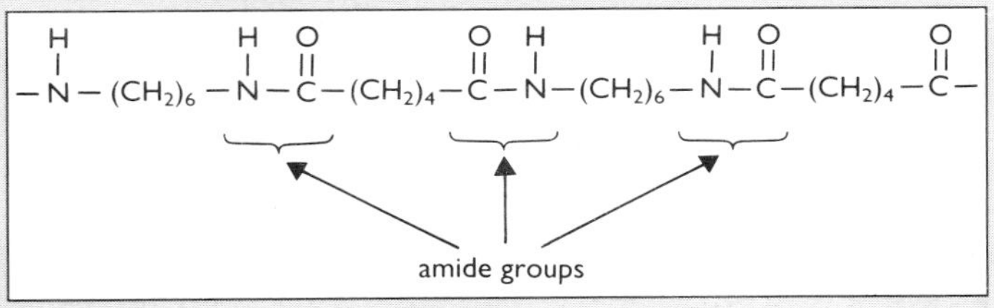

amide groups

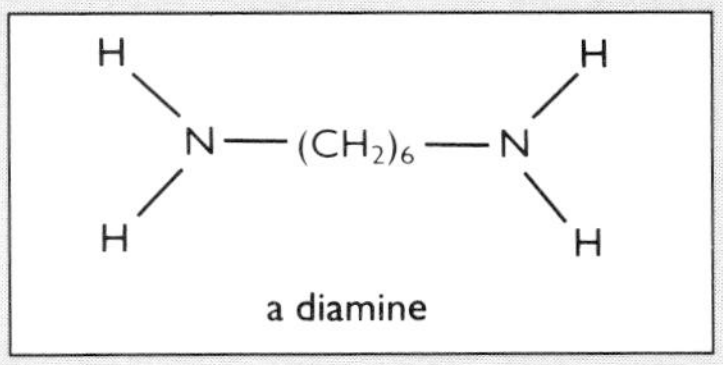

a diamine

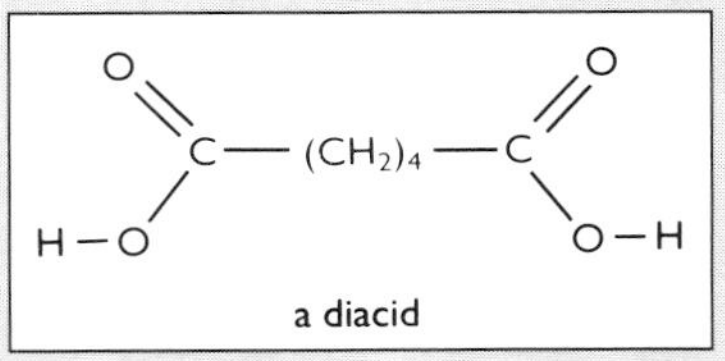

a diacid

Notice that the monomers contain two functional groups per molecule. Condensation can then occur at both ends of each molecule enabling a long chain to be constructed.

Polyester fibre also illustrates this point. It is synthesised by condensation of two monomers, one having two hydroxyl groups is called a *diol* and the other is a *diacid*. Their formulae are on the left.

The diacid used to make polyester is different from that used in nylon manufacture.

The structure of polyester, obtained by condensing two diol molecules and two diacid molecules, is shown below.

H—O—CH₂CH₂—O—H

a diol

a diacid

$-O-CH_2CH_2-O-\overset{O}{\underset{\|}{C}}-C_6H_4-\overset{O}{\underset{\|}{C}}-O-CH_2CH_2-O-\overset{O}{\underset{\|}{C}}-C_6H_4-\overset{O}{\underset{\|}{C}}-$

ISOMERS: STRUCTURAL FORMULAE AND NAMING

Isomers are compounds which have the same molecular formula but different structural formulae.

Butane, molecular formula C_4H_{10}, has two isomers. Their structural formulae, both full and shortened, are shown on the left.

Compound A is called butane and is an example of a straight-chain hydrocarbon. Compound B is a branched hydrocarbon and its name is 2-methylpropane. The method of naming this compound follows a system laid down by the International Union of Pure and Applied Chemistry (IUPAC) and operates as follows.

CH₃CH₂CH₂CH₃

A

(1) Select the longest chain of carbon atoms in the molecule and name this chain after the appropriate compound.

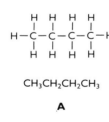

CH₃
|
CH₃CHCH₃

B

(2) Find out which atom the branch is attached to by giving each carbon in the longest chain a number. Begin numbering from the end which is nearer the branch.

(3) Identify the branch, i.e. whether it is a methyl group (CH₃−) or ethyl group (C₂H₅ −) etc.

How this system applies to the above example is illustrated in figure 2.

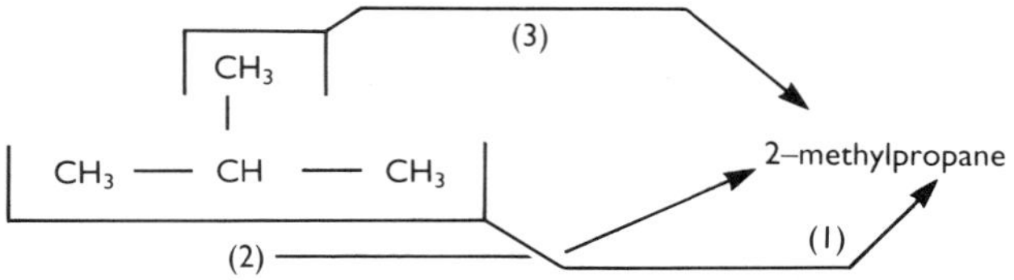
(3)
CH_3
CH_3 — CH — CH_3
2–methylpropane
(1)
(2)

Figure 2

Pentane has three isomers as follows (boiling points given in brackets).

pentane (36°C) | 2–methylbutane (28°C) | 2, 2–dimethylpropane (10°C)

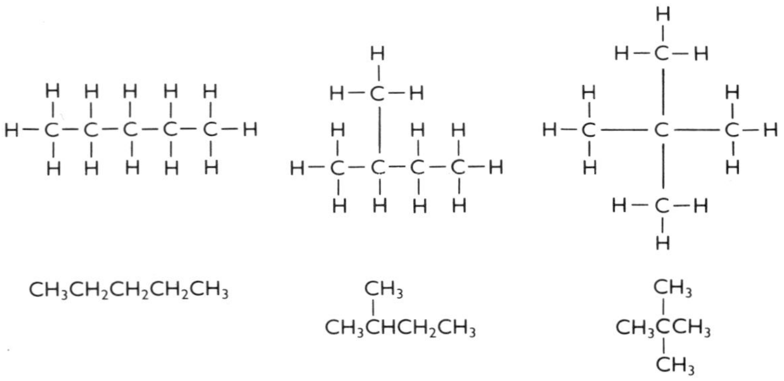
$CH_3CH_2CH_2CH_2CH_3$
CH_3
$CH_3CHCH_2CH_3$
CH_3
CH_3CCH_3
CH_3

There is a tendency for the boiling point to decrease as the amount of branching increases, since this causes the molecule to become more compact and have a smaller surface area. The weak forces of attraction between the molecules are even less as a result.

The following structures are given to illustrate some of the problems which arise when dealing with structural formulae. The same isomer can often be represented in several different ways:

a) writing the branch below instead of above the carbon atom chain, or
b) numbering from the wrong end, or
c) drawing a bend in the longest chain.

It is important to be able to recognise the isomer whichever way it is drawn. The structural formulae on the right show different ways of representing the same isomer, namely, 2–methylbutane.

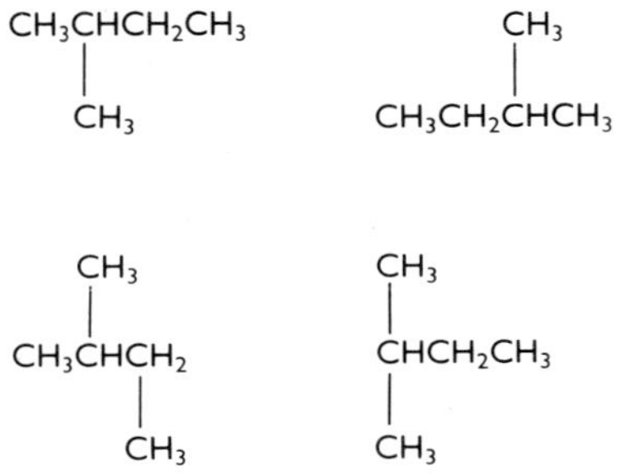
$CH_3CHCH_2CH_3$
CH_3
CH_3
$CH_3CH_2CHCH_3$
CH_3
CH_3CHCH_2
CH_3
CH_3
$CHCH_2CH_3$
CH_3

Many compounds were given a common or trivial name before the need for systematic naming was appreciated. For example, the branched isomer of butane was commonly known as iso-butane. In the following sections of this unit, trivial names will frequently be given in brackets after the systematic name.

The system of naming can be applied to more complicated molecules as shown by the following two examples.

1	2

$$CH_3 \quad CH_3$$
$$| \quad\quad |$$
$$CH_3CCH_2CHCH_3$$
$$|$$
$$CH_3$$

2, 2, 4–trimethylpentane

$$C_2H_5$$
$$|$$
$$CH_3CHCHCH_2CH_3$$
$$| \quad\quad |$$
$$CH_3 \quad CH_3$$

3–ethyl–2, 4–dimethylhexane
(an isomer of decane, $C_{10}H_{22}$)

Compound **1** is the standard by which fuels are given an octane rating.

ALKENES

In 1986 nearly 15 million tons of ethene were produced by the chemical industry in the USA. Only sulphuric acid, nitrogen and oxygen were produced in greater quantity that year. The second most important organic chemical was propene, ranked tenth with nearly 8 million tons produced. Both alkenes are very important starting materials in the petrochemical industry especially for the manufacture of polymers.

Ethene undergoes addition polymerisation to form poly(ethene) commonly known as polythene:

$$n\ CH_2{=}CH_2 \longrightarrow {-}[CH_2{-}CH_2]_n$$

ethene   poly(ethene)

Low density poly(ethene) or LDPE (0.92 g cm^{-3}) is made at very high pressures and at temperatures around 150–300°C in the presence of an initiator. Extensive branching of the chains occurs during manufacture, forming a more flexible material suitable for use in film packaging and electrical insulation.

High density poly(ethene) or HDPE ($0.96 \, g \, cm^{-3}$) is manufactured at much lower pressures and temperatures in the presence of catalysts containing either titanium or chromium compounds. The chains have very few branches so that the resulting polymer is stronger and more rigid that LDPE. It is used to make pipes, gutters, containers for household chemicals and in industrial packaging.

Another form known as linear low density poly(ethene) or LLDPE is made by a similar process to HDPE but involves copolymerisation of ethene with monomers such as butene to introduce side-chains into the polymer structure. Over 100 000 tons of LLDPE were manufacured in Scotland in 1990. It has the same uses as LDPE.

Ethene is used to make other monomers for the plastics industry. An important example is its reaction with benzene during the production of styrene which is then polymerised to form polystyrene.

The diol which is a monomer for the manufacture of the polyester mentioned on page 22 is made from ethene. This compound is also important as an antifreeze in car radiators since it lowers the freezing point of water when mixed with it.

Ethene is manufactured by a process called *steam cracking* from two different feedstocks, one being a gas, the other a liquid. The feedstocks are cracked at high temperatures (about 800°C) in the presence of steam. As well as ethene, fuel gases (namely, methane and hydrogen), propene and gasoline are produced.

The gaseous feedstock is usually ethane which has been separated from the gas fraction obtained during the distillation of crude oil. This fraction, often called 'natural gas liquids' or NGLs, is itself an alternative feedstock to ethane. The liquid feedstock is usually naphtha – a fraction obtained during the distillation of crude oil. It has a boiling point range of 70–180°C and contains hydrocarbons with 6–10 carbon atoms per molecule.

Both types of feedstock are cracked at Grangemouth while ethane is cracked at Mossmorran in Fife. Table 5 gives a comparison of the approximate percentages of the different products obtained on cracking these two feedstocks. While ethane provides a much greater percentage of ethene, naphtha produces higher proportions of valuable by-products.

Product	Approximate percentage obtained from cracking	
	Ethane	Naphtha
Ethene	80	30
Fuel gases (CH_4, H_2)	10	25
Propene	5	15
Gasoline	5	30

Table 5

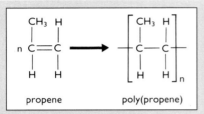

propene   poly(propene)

Propene which is produced during the steam cracking of naphtha and ethane or natural gas liquids is also a very important starting material for making polymers.

Propene is polymerised to form poly(propene), see left.

It can also be processed to form other monomers,

e.g. $CH_2 = \overset{\overset{\displaystyle CN}{|}}{CH}$, a compound called propenonitrile or acrylonitrile which is polymerised to give poly(acrylonitrile) an important synthetic fibre used in the textiles industry. This is commonly known as acrylic fibre.

Propene can also be converted into other useful chemicals such as propan–2–ol and propanone which will be mentioned in later sections of this unit, pages 33 and 36.

The production and major uses of ethene and propene are summarised in the flow diagram shown in figure 3.

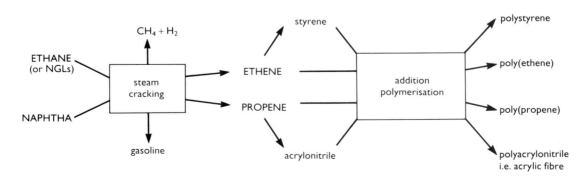

Figure 3 Production and uses of ethene and propene

NB: In several places within this unit information is illustrated by a flow diagram in which names of processes are enclosed in boxes. A rectangular box, e.g. $\boxed{\text{Cracking}}$, indicates a *chemical* process, while an oval box, e.g. $\bigcirc\!\!\!\text{Distillation}\!\!\!\bigcirc$, shows a *physical* process.

Isomers of alkenes can arise for two reasons. The position of the double bond can vary and the chain can be straight or branched. This is illustrated by the following examples which are isomers of butene, C_4H_8.

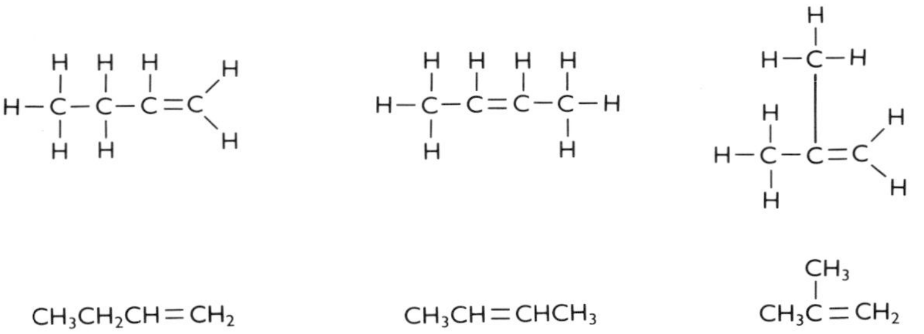

$CH_3CH_2CH=CH_2$

but–1–ene

$CH_3CH=CHCH_3$

but–2–ene

$CH_3C=CH_2$ (with CH_3 branch)

2–methylpropene

Where necessary, the name shows the position of the double bond. Thus but–2–ene has the double bond between the second and third carbon atoms in the chain.

When naming a branched alkene the position of the double bond is all important. The name of the alkene whose structure is shown on the right, is 3–methylbut–1–ene (and *not* 2–methylbut–3–ene). Numbering the carbon atoms from the right hand end of the chain gives the lowest number, in this case 1, to indicate the position of the double bond and consequently the methyl branch is attached at the third carbon atom.

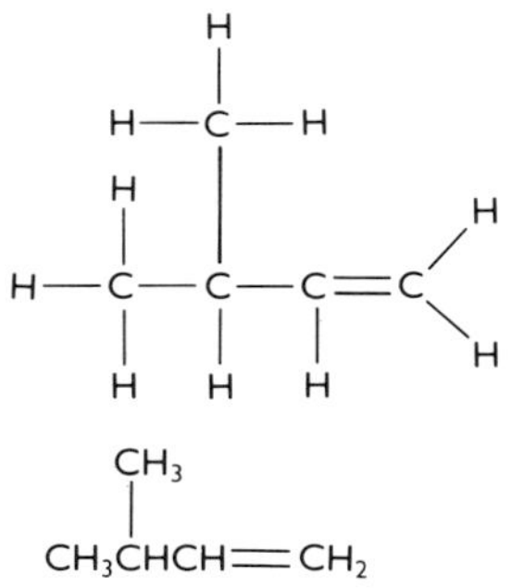

$CH_3CHCH=CH_2$ (with CH_3 branch)

3 –methylbut-1-ene

AROMATIC HYDROCARBONS

Naphtha is also an important feedstock for the production of a group of compounds known as aromatic hydrocarbons. Steam cracking of naphtha, page 25, yields a small proportion of aromatic compounds.

Cyclohexane, which is present in naphtha, can undergo *dehydrogenation* or removal of hydrogen to produce benzene, which is the simplest aromatic hydrocarbon.

$$C_6H_{12} \rightarrow C_6H_6 + 3H_2$$
Cyclohexane   Benzene

27

This process is an example of *reforming* and involves passing the naphtha fraction over a catalyst, platinum or molybdenum(VI) oxide, at about 500°C. Straight-chain alkanes may also be converted to aromatic hydrocarbons, e.g. heptane undergoes *cyclisation* or ring formation as well as dehydrogenation to form methylbenzene or toluene.

$$C_7H_{16} \quad \rightarrow \quad C_7H_8 \quad + \; 4H_2$$
$$\text{Heptane} \quad \text{Methylbenzene}$$

benzene:

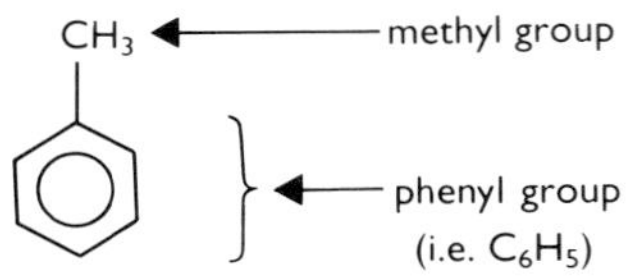

Benzene has a ring structure which is usually drawn as shown on the left. Each corner of the hexagon represents a carbon atom with a hydrogen atom attached. Methylbenzene (toluene), $C_6H_5CH_3$, has one of these hydrogen atoms replaced by a methyl group as illustrated.

This formula also shows what is meant by the term '*phenyl* group' which is present in many aromatic compounds. It consists of a benzene ring minus one hydrogen atom and, of course, must be attached to another atom or group of atoms. The prefix 'phenyl' is sometimes used in naming aromatic compounds. For example, phenylethene is the systematic name for styrene which is the monomer for producing polystyrene or poly(phenylethene) as follows.

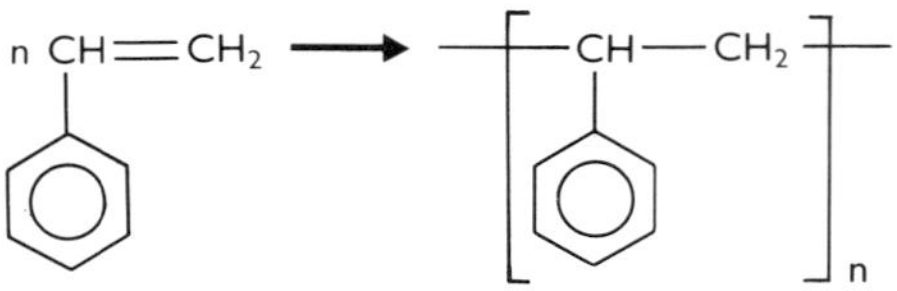

methylbenzene:

CH₃ ◄——— methyl group

phenyl group
(i.e. C₆H₅)

n CH═CH₂ ⟶

phenylethene
(styrene)

poly(phenylethene)
(polystyrene)

It is possible to have more than one of the hydrogen atoms in benzene replaced by methyl groups, e.g. 1, 4 dimethylbenzene or para–xylene.

This compound can be oxidised to form the diacid required as a monomer for the production of polyester mentioned earlier on page 22.

Refer to table 1 and from the structural formulae identify those consumer products which contain a benzene ring and hence are aromatic. Table 6 shows some simple aromatic compounds and indicates some of their uses.

CH₃──◯──CH₃

CH₃C₆H₄CH₃

1, 4–dimethylbenzene

Name	Phenol	Benzoic acid	Phenylamine (Aniline)
Formulae	$\langle O \rangle$—OH C_6H_5OH	$\langle O \rangle$—COOH C_6H_5COOH	$\langle O \rangle$—NH$_2$ $C_6H_5NH_2$

Uses	Manufacture of
	  Bakelite and phenolic resins
	  Monomers for making
	    nylon
	  Germicides (e.g. Dettol,
	    TCP)
	  Drugs (e.g. Aspirin) and
	    dyes
		Food additive, E210
		(preservative and
		antioxidant, as are
		its salts E211–219)
			Manufacture of dyes and
			drugs

Table 6

The most important use of benzene itself is in making styrene. Benzene is also used to produce monomers for nylon manufacture and in the production of detergents.

Although aromatic compounds can be derived from petroleum as outlined above, this is not the only source. If coal is heated in the absence of air, a process sometimes called *destructive distillation* occurs which yields several useful materials as shown in figure 4.

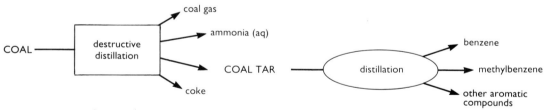

Figure 4 Products from coal

Coal tar is a mixture mainly comprising aromatic compounds. For many years before the 'oil boom' this was the main source of benzene and related compounds. According to present estimates, coal reserves are expected to outlast oil reserves and hence coal may well regain its importance as a source of aromatic compounds.

From its formula, C_6H_6, it might have been expected that benzene would be unsaturated. Indeed, a possible structural formula frequently seen in organic chemistry textbooks shows an arrangement of alternate double and single bonds (see next page).

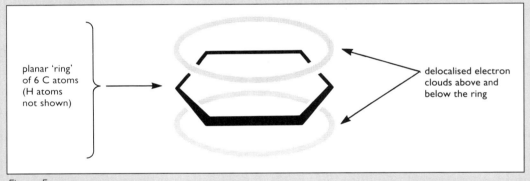

However, if an aromatic hydrocarbon is shaken up with bromine water rapid decolouration does *not* occur. This indicates that $C = C$ bonds are not present. In benzene each carbon atom uses up three of its four outer electrons in forming bonds with a hydrogen atom and two adjacent carbon atoms. The six remaining electrons, one from each carbon atom, occupy electron clouds which are not confined or localised between any one pair of carbon atoms. These electrons are said to be *delocalised*, see figure 5.

planar 'ring' of 6 C atoms (H atoms not shown) → delocalised electron clouds above and below the ring

Figure 5

The delocalised electrons give additional bonding strength. As you can see from the data on mean bond enthalpies given in table 7, the carbon–carbon bond in benzene is stronger than the $C—C$ bond but weaker than the $C=C$ bond.

Bond	Mean bond enthalpy / kJ mol^{-1}	Bond length / pm = 10^{-12} m
C—C	337	154
C=C	607	134
C—C (aromatic)	519	139

Table 7

Table 7 also shows that the carbon–carbon bond length, that is the distance between the nuclei of carbon atoms which are bonded together, is greater than the $C=C$ bond length but less than that of the $C—C$ bond.

All the carbon–carbon bonds in benzene are of equal length. Therefore it is considered appropriate to represent the structure of benzene as a regular hexagon. The circle inside the hexagon indicates the additional bonding due to the delocalised electrons.

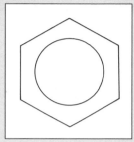

The benzene ring only undergoes addition reactions with some difficulty. This point is confirmed by the chemistry of aromatic compounds discussed above and the fact that a large number of stable compounds incorporate this group of atoms.

Addition reactions of benzene, however, do occur. Hydrogenation of benzene produces cyclohexane. Benzene reacts with chlorine under certain conditions to form an important insecticide, benzene hexachloride or BHC, formula: $C_6H_6Cl_6$.

ALKANOLS

As you know from earlier work, ethanol can be produced from carbohydrates by fermentation catalysed by enzymes present in yeast. The overall process can be represented by a simple equation:

$$C_6H_{12}O_6 \rightarrow 2C_2H_5OH + 2CO_2$$
$$\text{Glucose} \qquad \text{Ethanol}$$

While this is the most important process for making alcohol for human consumption, industrial demand for ethanol is such that other methods have been developed.

The most important way of achieving this is by *catalytic hydration* of ethene, i.e. the addition of water in the presence of a catalyst.

$$CH_2 = CH_2 + H_2O \rightarrow C_2H_5OH$$

A mixture of ethene and steam is pressurised (at about 65 atmospheres) and passed over a catalyst (phosphoric acid) at 300°C. Only about 5% conversion of ethene is achieved under these conditions. However, unreacted ethene is separated from the liquid products and recycled to give a 95% yield of ethanol. This method can be applied to the production of other alkanols from alkenes with more carbon atoms.

The reverse process, i.e. *dehydration* of an alkanol, can be easily demonstrated in the laboratory using the apparatus illustrated in figure 6.

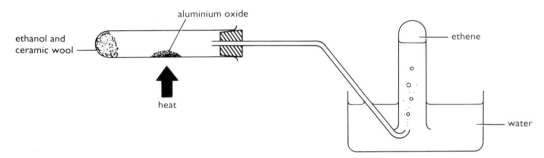

Figure 6 Dehydration of ethanol

When ethanol vapour is passed over hot aluminium oxide, which acts as a catalyst, dehydration occurs forming ethene.

$$C_2H_5OH \rightarrow CH_2 = CH_2 + H_2O$$

This process is not confined to the production of ethene. Other alkenes can be produced by dehydration of higher alkanols. Concentrated sulphuric acid has a strong attraction for water and can also be used to dehydrate alkanols.

While ethanol is a very important organic chemical, it should be realised that it is only one member of the homologous series of alkanols. Table 8 gives the names and formulae of several alkanols and illustrates the fact that there are different *types* of alkanols – primary, secondary and tertiary – which arise from the position of the –OH group on the carbon chain.

Name of alkanol	Molecular formula	Structural formula		Type of alkanol
Methanol	CH_3OH			Primary
Ethanol	C_2H_5OH	CH_3CH_2OH 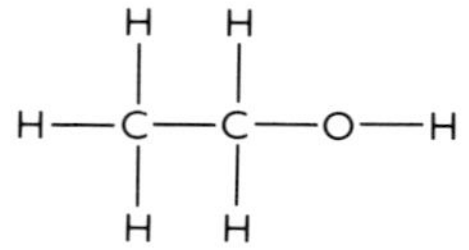		Primary
Propan–1–ol	C_3H_7OH	$CH_3CH_2CH_2OH$ 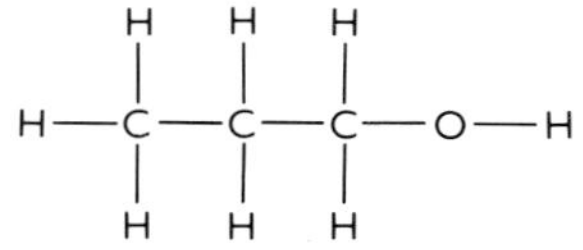		Primary
Propan–2–ol	C_3H_7OH	CH_3CHCH_3 OH		Secondary
Butan–1–ol	C_4H_9OH	$CH_3CH_2CH_2CH_2OH$		Primary
Butan–2–ol	C_4H_9OH	$CH_3CH_2CHCH_3$ OH		Secondary
2–Methylpropan–2–ol	C_4H_9OH	CH_3 CH_3-C-CH_3 OH		Tertiary
General formula:	$C_nH_{2n+1}OH$			

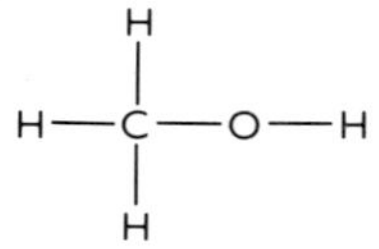

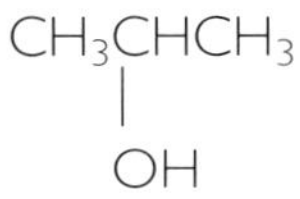

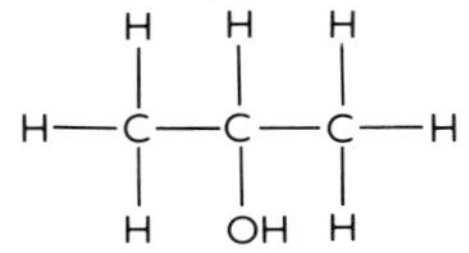

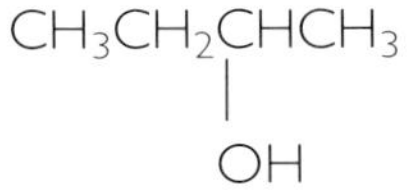

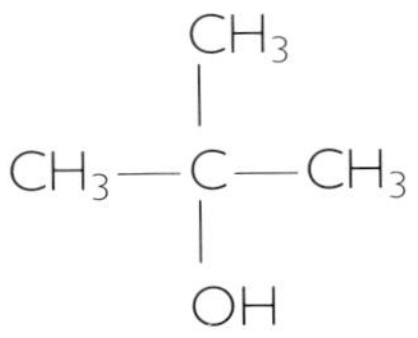

Table 8

When naming an alkanol it is usually necessary to specify the carbon atom to which the –OH group is attached. The name of the last compound in table 8 is related to its structure as shown on the next page.

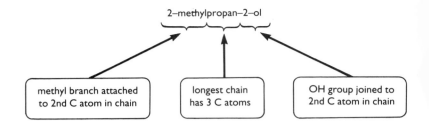

Table 9 summarises the main points regarding the structure of different types of alkanol.

Type	Position of –OH group	Characteristic group of atoms	General formula
Primary	Attached to the *end* of the carbon chain	$-CH_2OH$	$R-CH_2OH$
Secondary	Attached to an *intermediate* C atom	$\diagdown\!\!\diagup CHOH$	$\begin{smallmatrix}R'\\\diagdown\\\diagup\\R\end{smallmatrix}CHOH$
Tertiary	Attached to an intermediate C atom which also has a *branch*	$-\overset{\mid}{\underset{\mid}{C}}OH$	$R-\overset{R'}{\underset{R''}{\overset{\mid}{\underset{\mid}{C}}}}OH$

Table 9

R, R' and R" represent *alkyl groups* such as methyl, CH_3- and ethyl, C_2H_5-. In an alkanol these groups may be the same, as in propan–2–ol, or different, as in butan–2–ol. In 2–methylpropan–2–ol all three alkyl groups are the same, namely, methyl groups.

METHANOL

On page 32 it was pointed out that, in general, alkanols can be prepared by hydration of the appropriate alkene. This is, of course, not possible for methanol since the simplest alkene has two carbon atoms.

Industrially, methanol is made from *synthesis gas* which is a mixture of carbon monoxide and hydrogen. Synthesis gas is made by a process called *steam reforming* in which methane and steam are passed over a nickel catalyst at around 900°C.

$$CH_4(g) + H_2O(g) \rightarrow CO(g) + 3H_2(g)$$

The hydrogen content of synthesis gas is then adjusted and the mixture of carbon monoxide and hydrogen passed over a second catalyst, usually zinc(II) oxide and chromium(III) oxide at a temperature of 300°C and a pressure of 300 atmospheres. The reaction is shown in the following equation.

$$CO(g) + 2H_2(g) \rightarrow CH_3OH(g)$$

Methanol is oxidised to methanal for making thermosetting plastics. Synthesis gas can also be used to provide hydrogen for the manufacture of ammonia by the Haber process.

OXIDATION OF ALKANOLS

Primary and secondary alkanols can be oxidised by various oxidising agents but tertiary alkanols do not readily undergo oxidation. Acidified potassium dichromate solution is a suitable oxidising agent. When mixed with a primary (or secondary) alkanol and heated in a water bath, the orange colour due to dichromate ions changes to a blue-green colour showing that chromium(III) ions have been formed. A different smell may be detected showing that the alkanol has changed. The reduction of dichromate ions to chromium(III) ions can be expressed in the following ion–electron equation.

$$\underset{\text{Dichromate}}{Cr_2O_7^{2-}} + 14H^+ + 6e^- \rightarrow \underset{\text{Chromium(III)}}{2Cr^{3+}} + 7H_2O$$

Oxidation can also be achieved by passing the alkanol vapour over heated copper(II) oxide as shown in figure 7. During the reaction the oxide is reduced to copper.

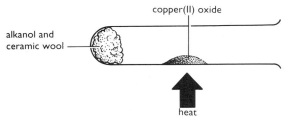

Figure 7 Oxidation of an alkanol

Primary alkanols are oxidised to *alkanals*

e.g. Ethanol → Ethanal (Acetaldehyde)

$CH_3CH_2OH \rightarrow CH_3CHO$

i.e.

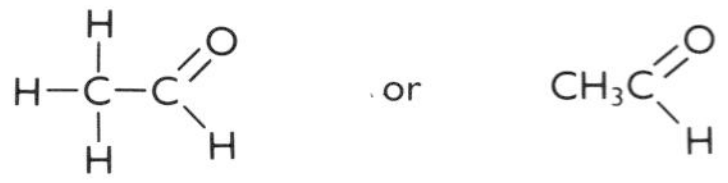

Propan–l–ol → Propanal

$CH_3CH_2CH_2OH \rightarrow CH_3CH_2CHO$

i.e.

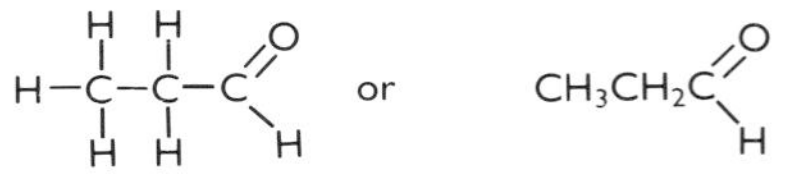

In general:

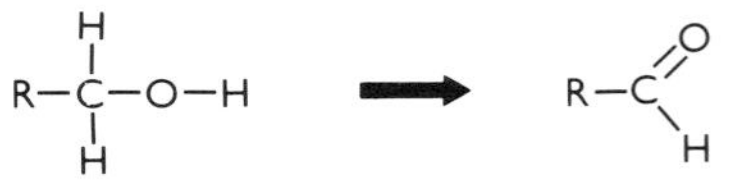

primary alkanols　　alkanals

Secondary alkanols are oxidised to *alkanones*

e.g. Propan–2–ol → Propanone (Acetone)

$CH_3\underset{\displaystyle OH}{\underset{|}{C}}H\,CH_3 \rightarrow CH_3\underset{\displaystyle O}{\underset{\|}{C}}\,CH_3$ i.e.

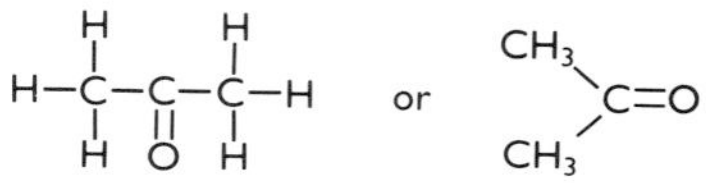

Butan–2–ol → Butan–2–one

$CH_3CH_2\underset{\displaystyle OH}{\underset{|}{C}}H\,CH_3 \rightarrow CH_3CH_2\underset{\displaystyle O}{\underset{\|}{C}}\,CH_3$ i.e.

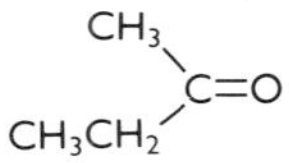

In general:

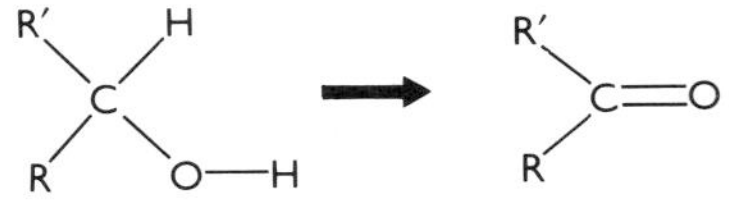

secondary alkanols　　alkanones

Alkanals and alkanones both contain a carbon–oxygen double bond, C = O, which is known as the *carbonyl* group. In an alkanal, the carbonyl group is at the end of the carbon chain and has a hydrogen atom attached to it. In an alkanone the carbonyl group is joined to carbon atoms, and hence alkyl groups, on both sides. Alkanals and alkanones are two further examples of homologous series. Table 10 indicates the functional group, general formula and first member of each series.

	Alkanals	Alkanones
Functional Group	CHO ; $-C\overset{\displaystyle O}{\underset{\displaystyle H}{\diagup}}$	$\diagdown CO$; $\diagup C = O$
General Formula	$C_nH_{2n}O$ (where $n \geqslant 1$)	$C_nH_{2n}O$ (where $n \geqslant 3$)
First Member	$HCHO$; $H-C\overset{\displaystyle O}{\underset{\displaystyle H}{\diagup}}$ Methanal (Formaldehyde)	CH_3COCH_3 ; $CH_3 \diagdown C = O \diagup CH_3$ Propanone (Acetone)

Table 10

Alkanals and alkanones which possess the same number of carbon atoms will be isomers. For example, propanal and propanone are isomers although they belong to different homologous series.

Compounds which contain the –CHO group are more generally known as *aldehydes*. These include unsaturated aldehydes and aromatic aldehydes as well as alkanals. Similarly, alkanones are a sub-set of a more general series known as *ketones*.

Alkanals and alkanones can be distinguished by attempting to carry out further oxidation. Alkanals are readily oxidised to *alkanoic acids* (carboxylic acids). Alkanones are difficult to oxidise. The reducing properties of an alkanal can be shown when added to various oxidising agents and heated gently in a water bath. Suitable oxidising agents are listed in table 11 which also gives an explanation of the results obtained.

Since they are not readily oxidised, alkanones do not react with these reagents.

Acidified dichromate oxidises alkanals to alkanoic acids. The other two oxidising agents are alkaline, hence they will oxidise alkanals to the appropriate alkanoate ions.

Oxidising agent	Observations and explanations
1 Benedict's or Fehling's solution	Blue solution $\rightarrow$ Orange–red precipitate; Cu^{2+} ions reduced to Cu_2O i.e. copper (I) oxide
2 Tollen's reagent i.e. $AgNO_3(aq) + NH_3(aq)$	A silver mirror is formed; Ag^+ ions reduced to Ag atoms
3 Acidified potassium dichromate solution	Orange solution $\rightarrow$ blue–green solution; $Cr_2O_7{}^{2-}$ reduced to Cr^{3+}

Table 11

Methanal on oxidation gives *methanoic acid* (formic acid)

$$HCHO \text{ or } H-C \overset{O}{\underset{H}{<}} \rightarrow HCOOH \text{ or } H-C \overset{O}{\underset{O-H}{<}}$$

Ethanal on oxidation gives *ethanoic acid* (acetic acid)

$$CH_3CHO \text{ or } CH_3-C \overset{O}{\underset{H}{<}} \rightarrow CH_3COOH \text{ or } CH_3-C \overset{O}{\underset{O-H}{<}}$$

Propanal gives propanoic acid, butanal gives butanoic acid and so on. Alkanoic acids form another homologous series.

Functional group: $-COOH$ or $-C \overset{O}{\underset{O-H}{<}}$

General formula: $C_nH_{2n}O_2$

Ethanoic acid is the most important member of the series. Vinegar, which is a solution of ethanoic acid (about 5% concentration), is made by bacterial oxidation of beer or poor quality wines. Enzymes in the bacteria help the ethanol to react with oxygen from the air.

However, ethanoic acid can also be made by direct oxidation of alkanes from oil. The feedstock is either butane or naphtha and the process is carried out under pressure (about 50 atmospheres) and at around 180°C. While ethanoic acid is the main product, other acids (methanoic and propanoic) as well as propanone are produced in large amounts.

CONDENSATION POLYMERS FROM METHANAL

Methanal is an important monomer in the synthesis of thermosetting plastics. Bakelite is manufactured by reaction of phenol with methanal. This is an example of *condensation polymerisation*, in which the oxygen atom of methanal combines with hydrogen atoms from the phenyl group to form water as shown below:

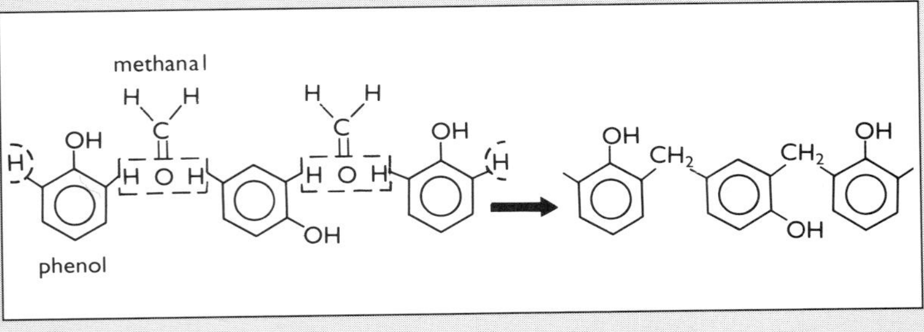

The reaction does not stop at this stage. Further condensation between methanal and phenol results in the cross-linking of chains to form a 3–dimensional network. This gives a highly rigid structure which does not soften on heating. Hence it is a thermosetting plastic.

A similar material is formed by condensation between methanal and carbamide (urea), NH_2CONH_2. The resulting thermoset has the advantage of being white whereas bakelite is nearly black.

These polymers have a variety of applications where a rigid plastic is required, e.g. handles for cooking utensils and irons, 'formica' table tops, bathroom and electrical fitments.

FUELS FROM OIL

Coal and natural gas can, of course, be used directly as fuels, although coal usually has to be converted into smokeless fuel for use in cities. In contrast, crude oil is not itself suitable as a source of energy unless it has been processed. However, once it has been processed it yields a variety of fuels.

The first stage of refining oil is often called primary distillation in which the components, or fractions, of crude oil are separated out by their differing boiling points, as shown in figure 8. Further separation of the residue is achieved under reduced pressure by a process called vacuum distillation.

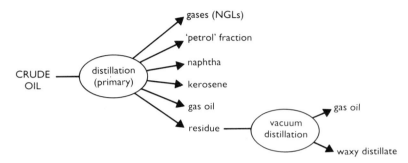

Figure 8 Fractions from crude oil

The fractions so obtained are still not ready to be used as fuels but require further processing. Straight-chain hydrocarbons do not perform well as fuel in a petrol-burning engine. Better performance occurs if aromatic hydrocarbons as well as branched-chain hydrocarbons are incorporated in the petrol.

Unleaded petrol requires an even greater degree of molecular branching and aromatic content. Leaded petrol contains the anti-knocking agent, lead tetra-ethyl, $Pb(C_2H_5)_4$. Dibromoethane is also added to act as a scavenger for lead by producing volatile lead(II) bromide which escapes in the exhaust fumes.

The petrol fraction or 'light gasoline' obtained on distillation of crude oil contains no aromatic hydrocarbons and not enough branched-chain hydrocarbons to make it an efficient fuel on its own. Catalytic reforming of the naphtha fraction has already been mentioned in an earlier section, page 28, as a means of producing aromatic hydrocarbons such as benzene from naphtha. Reforming also includes processes in which molecular rearrangement or isomerisation occurs, i.e. where the number of atoms per molecule do not change. In particular, straight-chain hydrocarbons undergo rearrangement to form branched-chain hydrocarbons as illustrated by the following example.

$$CH_3CH_2CH_2CH_2CH_2CH_2CH_2CH_3 \rightarrow$$

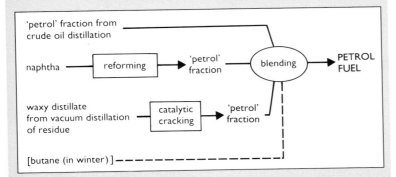

octane   2,2,4–trimethylpentane

The products obtained on reforming naphtha as well as those from the catalytic cracking of heavier fractions are blended with the petrol fraction to give a more efficient fuel. Butane is added in winter to make the fuel more volatile. The flow diagram shown in figure 9 summarises how petrol is made.

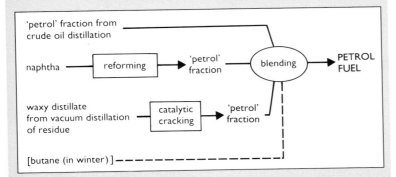

Figure 9   Making petrol

Chemical processes are not required to produce diesel. It is made by blending gas oil fractions obtained (i) by primary distillation of crude oil and (ii) by vacuum distillation of the residue from the primary distillation, as shown in figure 10. A small amount of kerosene may also be added during manufacture, especially in winter, to prevent the fuel freezing.

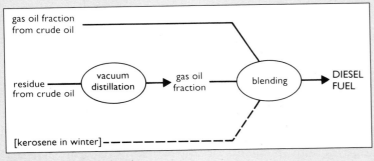

Figure 10   Making diesel

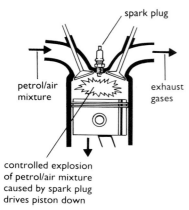

controlled explosion
of petrol/air mixture
caused by spark plug
drives piston down

Figure 11 Petrol engine

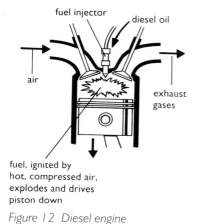

fuel, ignited by
hot, compressed air,
explodes and drives
piston down

Figure 12 Diesel engine

Petrol and diesel oil are the most important fuels for use in internal combustion engines. Although there are similarities, petrol and diesel engines have significant differences especially in the method of ignition as can be seen from a close look at the diagrams. In a petrol engine, a mixture of petrol vapour and air is drawn into the cylinder, compressed and ignited by a high voltage electric spark, as shown in figure 11. Diesel fuel, on the other hand, is less volatile since it has larger molecules. It is injected into the cylinder and ignites in the air which has been heated by compression. Note the absence of a spark-plug in figure 12.

One of the major disadvantages of fossil fuels, such as oil, coal and natural gas, is that they are not renewable. Ethanol, which can be produced by fermentation from renewable resources, is therefore being used increasingly as a blending agent in motor fuel. For example, 'Gasohol' is a lead-free petrol containing between 10% and 20% ethanol. The use of ethanol as a fuel is being encouraged in certain countries, such as Brazil, where it is economic to produce it by fermentation. Thus sugar cane can be regarded as a renewable source of ethanol for engine fuel.

You already know that combustion of fuels yields products which may damage the environment. Incomplete combustion produces the toxic gas carbon monoxide, while leaded petrol releases lead compounds even when fully burned. Any sulphur compounds present in the fuel will release sulphur dioxide into the atmosphere when the fuel burns. The sparking of air in a petrol engine produces oxides of nitrogen ('NO_X gases') which contribute to the problem of 'acid rain'. These gases are not produced in a diesel engine. However, it may well be that the single most harmful effect on the environment arises from the vast quantities of carbon dioxide contributing to the 'greenhouse effect'.

GASEOUS FUELS

Gaseous hydrocarbons are also important fuels and are obtained from two main sources, natural gas and crude oil. While methane is the major constituent of natural gas, significant quantities of ethane are also present. Since natural gas reserves are expected to decline, research is being carried out on other resources such as coal to develop ways of making 'substitute natural gas' or SNG.

Natural gas liquids (NGLs), the gas fraction obtained by distilling crude oil, can be further separated to yield not only methane and ethane but also propane and butane. The latter two gases are each blended with stocks derived from the cracking of heavier oil fractions and sold under the name 'liquified petroleum gas' or LPG. The LPG which consists mainly of propane is used for cutting and welding while the butane-based gas is used as a fuel for heating and cooking. The production of these fuels is summarised in the flow diagram shown in figure 13.

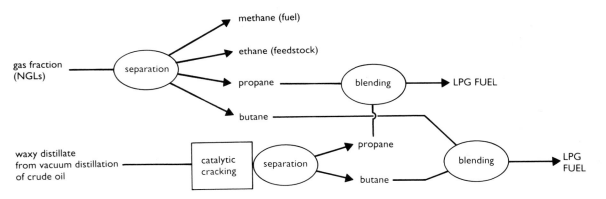

Figure 13 Making LPG

When vegetable and animal matter decays in the absence of air, *anaerobic respiration* occurs with the formation of a gaseous mixture known as *biogas*. This consists mainly of methane (about 60%) and carbon dioxide. It is a useful fuel especially in rural areas. On a farm, manure and straw can be fed into a large tank called a biogas digester, see figure 14.

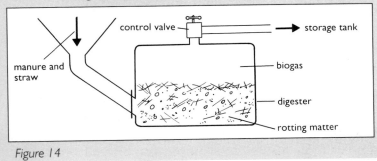

Figure 14

> Biogas is produced by the action of bacteria on the decaying matter. The bacteria function best in warm conditions, about 35°C. Hence in colder countries some of the biogas is used to keep the digester sufficiently warm. In China there are over 7 million biogas digesters providing energy for about five times that number of people.

A CAUTIONARY FOOTNOTE!

As a result of studying this unit you should be in a better position to appreciate the competing demands for carbon compounds as feedstocks or fuels. It is important that you realise that the quantity of carbon compounds used for fuels currently far outweighs that used for feedstocks.

However it should also be recognised that the chemical industry does not stand still. This unit describes the situation at the time of writing, but advances in technology as well as changes in supply and demand can alter the picture in a relatively short time.

Examples for practice

Access to a molecular model kit may be helpful especially in questions 1, 4, 6, 7, 8 and 9.

1. Write the structural formulae and systematic names of all five isomers of hexane. (5)

2. Write the structural formula of
(a) 2,4–dimethylheptane
(b) 3–ethyl–2–methylpentane. (2)

3. Write the systematic names of
(a)

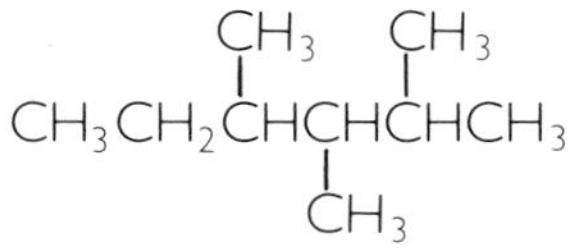

$$CH_3CH_2CHCHCHCH_3$$
with CH_3, CH_3 above and CH_3 below

(b)

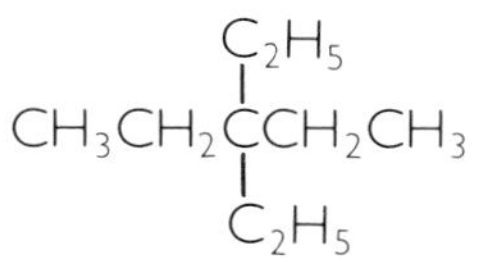

$$CH_3CH_2CCH_2CH_3$$
with C_2H_5 above and C_2H_5 below (2)

4. Write the structural formulae and systematic names of 3 isomers of pentene. (3)

5. Refer to pages 24 to 25 and present the information about the different types of poly(ethene) in a table with suitable headings. [PS](3)

6. 4–Methylpent–1–ene can be made from propene and then copolymerised with ethene to produce linear low density polyethene (LLDPE).
(a) Draw the structural formula of 4–methylpent–1–ene. (1)
(b) With the help of a molecular model kit, suggest how a molecule of this compound can be made from propene molecules. [PS](2)
(c) Draw a section of the structure of LLDPE formed by combining two molecules of ethene with one of 4–methylpent–1– ene. (2)
(Total: 5)

7. The full systematic name of the compound formed when propene reacts with bromine is 1,2–dibromopropane (see page 20).
(a) Write the structural formulae and systematic names of 2 more isomers of dibromopropane. (2)
(b) Explain why neither of these isomers is formed when propene reacts with bromine. [PS](2)
(Total: 4)

8. Copy the following carbon skeleton into your answer book *three* times.

$$-\overset{|}{\underset{|}{C}}-$$
$$-\overset{|}{\underset{|}{C}}-\overset{|}{\underset{|}{C}}-\overset{|}{\underset{|}{C}}-\overset{|}{\underset{|}{C}}-$$

Add a hydroxyl group to each skeleton to make
(a) a primary alkanol;
(b) a secondary alkanol;
(c) a tertiary alkanol. (SEB)(3)

9. There is one more isomer of butanol not listed in table 8 page 33. Draw its structural formula. Give its systematic name and decide what type of alkanol it is. (2)

10. Give the structural formula and type of each of the following alkanols.
(a) Pentan–3–ol   (b) 2–methylbutan–1–ol
(c) 3–ethylpentan–3–ol. (3)

11. Give the systematic name and type of each of the following alkanols. (2)

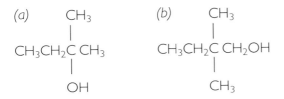

12. (a) Which letters in the grid below represent either the formula or the name of
(i) an amine,
(ii) a secondary alkanol,
(iii) an alkanal? (2)

CH₃CHCH₃ $\mid$ OH **A**	Butanone **B**
CH₃CH₂NH₂ **C**	$H-C\overset{\displaystyle O}{\underset{\displaystyle O-H}{}}$ **D**
$CH_3CH_2C\overset{\displaystyle O}{\underset{\displaystyle H}{}}$ **E**	Propan–1–ol **F**
$\overset{\displaystyle CH_3}{\underset{\displaystyle CH_3}{}}\!\!\diagdown\!\!\diagup C=O$ **G**	Methanal **H**

(b) Classify the remaining compounds in the grid. (2)
(c) Which letters represent the product of oxidation of
(i) A   (ii) F   (iii) H? (2)
(d) Which letters represent a compound which
(i) reacts with Benedict's solution,
(ii) forms a deep-blue colour with copper(II) sulphate solution? (2)
(e) Which letters represent a compound which when added to water will give a pH
(i) less than 7,
(ii) more than 7? (2)
(Total: 10)

13. Draw the structural formula of
    (a) 2–methylpropanal
    (b) 4–methylpentan–2–one
    (c) 3–methylbutanoic acid. (3)
    (Hint: Decide on the position of the
    functional group before adding the branch.)

14. (a) Draw the structural formula of
    (i) pentan–3–one
    (ii) pentanal
    (iii) pentanoic acid. (3)
    (b) Explain why a number is included in the
    name of compound (i) but not in the names
    of (ii) and (iii). [PS](2)
    (c) Name the alkanols which on oxidation
    would give the above compounds. (1)
    (Total: 6)

15. (a) Which letters in the grid below represent
    compounds which are aromatic. (4)
    (b) Which two letters represent isomers? (1)

(c) Which letters represent compounds which will
undergo addition reactions with bromine? (1)
(d) Which letter represents the compound with
    (i) the lowest molecular mass,
    (ii) the highest molecular mass? (2)
(e) Which letters represent compounds likely to
be present in the naphtha fraction obtained from
petroleum? (2)
(f) Choose two letters which represent
compounds likely to be produced when naphtha
undergoes reforming. (1)
(Total: 11)

16. Naphtha fractions from a distillation column
    contain a mixture of many hydrocarbons with
    a low octane rating. To improve its qualities
    as a petrol (i.e. increase the octane rating) the
    naphtha is passed over a catalyst of aluminium
    oxide, coated with platinum.
        The three reactions shown on the next
    page are typical of the process.

Hexane
A

— OH
B

Cyclohexane
C

C_6H_5COOH
D

Methylbenzene
E

Hex–1–ene
F

Cyclohexene
G

$$CH_2 \!-\! CH_2$$
$$\big| \qquad \diagdown$$
$$\qquad \quad CH_2$$
$$CH_2 \!-\! CH_2 \diagup$$
H

C_6H_6
I

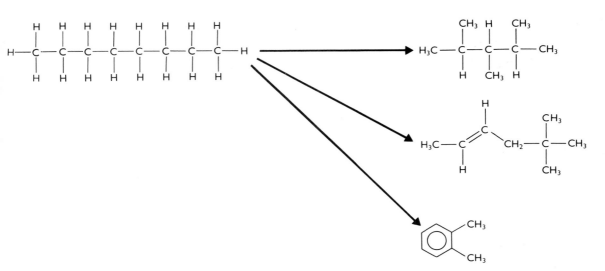

(a) What is the name given to this type of process? (1)

(b) Name the aromatic molecule in the above scheme. (1)

(c) Explain why this aromatic molecule, which has such a low H:C ratio, does *not* decolorise aqueous bromine quickly when they are shaken together. (1)

(SEB)(Total: 3)

3 Molecules to moles

From previous work you should *know* and *understand* the following.

a) How to write balanced equations and use them to calculate the mass of a reactant or product in a reaction.

b) How to calculate the formula mass of a compound and hence obtain its molar mass.

c) Concentration of a solution (see unit 1 introduction, part c).

d) How to carry out volumetric titrations and calculations related to them.

e) The processes of oxidation and reduction including reactions at the electrodes during electrolysis.

f) How to calculate an empirical formula from masses or percentage composition.

THE AVOGADRO CONSTANT AND THE MOLE

The *mole* is a very important quantity in chemistry since it enables us to compare amounts of different substances taking part in a chemical reaction. For example, magnesium and sulphur react together according to the following simple equation.

$$Mg + S \rightarrow MgS$$

The equation shows that this reaction needs equal numbers of magnesium and sulphur atoms. Since the elements differ in atomic mass, it will not be equal masses of each element that will combine.

Let us consider the three different elements listed in table 1.

The molar quantities contain the same number of atoms since they are in the same ratio as their atomic masses. This number is known as the *Avogadro Constant*, symbol L. It is a very large number but can be determined by experiment as we shall see in the next section.

	Magnesium	Sulphur	Iron
Mass of 1 atom (amu)	24	32	56
Mass of n atoms (amu)	24n	32n	56n
Ratio of mass of equal numbers of atoms	24	32	56
Mass of 1 mole	24 g	32 g	56 g

Table 1

In 1960 international agreement concerning the standard of atomic mass was achieved. It was agreed that the mass of the carbon–12 atom, $^{12}_{6}C$, should be exactly 12 atomic mass units (amu). All elements have atomic masses which are relative to this standard.

Hence a mole can be defined as the quantity of a substance which contains the same number of elementary entities as there are carbon atoms in 12 g of $^{12}_{6}C$. The elementary entities may be atoms, molecules, ions or other particles. Some examples are given below to illustrate this.

a) Metals and monatomic species, e.g. Noble gases.

Here the elementary entity is the *atom*.
Thus,   4 g of helium
        27 g of aluminium } each contain L atoms.
        197 g of gold

b) Covalent substances.

Here the elementary entity is the *molecule*.
To calculate the number of atoms it is necessary to multiply by the number of atoms per molecule as shown in table 2.

Quantity of substance	Formula	Number of molecules	Number of atoms per molecule	Number of atoms
2 g hydrogen	H_2	L	2	2L
18 g water	H_2O	L	3	3L
30 g ethane	C_2H_6	L	8	8L

Table 2

In the last example, L molecules of ethane contain 2 L atoms of carbon and 6 L atoms of hydrogen.

c) Ionic compounds

Here the elementary entity is more difficult to specify. It is the 'formula-unit' of *ions*. The total number of ions depends on the number in each formula. Table 3 illustrates this with 3 examples.

Quantity of substance	Formula	Number of 'formula units'	Number of positive and negative ions	Total number of ions
58.5 g sodium chloride	Na^+Cl^-	L	L sodium ions and L chloride ions	2L
148 g magnesium nitrate	$Mg^{2+}(NO_3^-)_2$	L	L magnesium ions and 2L nitrate ions	3L
342 g aluminium sulphate	$(Al^{3+})_2(SO_4^{2-})_3$	L	2L aluminium ions and 3L sulphate ions	5L

Table 3

QUANTITATIVE ELECTROLYSIS

Three cells containing respectively silver(I) nitrate solution, copper(II) sulphate solution and dilute hydrochloric acid are connected in series as shown in figure 1. Let us suppose that in a particular experiment a current of one amp is passed through the circuit for 965 seconds. Relevant data and results are shown in table 4.

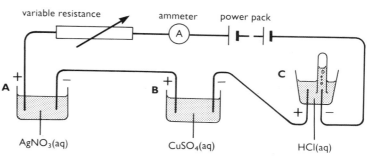

Figure 1

Cell:	A	B	C
Solution	Silver(I) nitrate	Copper(II) sulphate	Hydrochloric acid
Current/A	1.0	1.0	1.0
Time for which current passed/s	965	965	965
Quantity of electricity used/coulombs, C (= current × time)	965	965	965
Considering only the negative electrode in each cell:			
Product	Silver	Copper	Hydrogen
Ion-electron equation	$Ag^+ + e^- \rightarrow Ag$	$Cu^{2+} + 2e^- \rightarrow Cu$	$2H^+ + 2e^- \rightarrow H_2$
Mass of product/g	1.08	0.32	0.01
Mass of 1 mole of product/g	108	64	2
Number of moles of product	0.01	0.005	0.005
Quantity of electricity required to produce a mole of product/C	$\dfrac{965}{0.01}$ = 96500	$\dfrac{965}{0.005}$ = 193000	$\dfrac{965}{0.005}$ = 193000

Table 4

Thus, 96500 coulombs are needed to produce 1 mole of Ag from 1 mole of Ag^+. This quantity of charge is called the Faraday, named after an English scientist. Production of 1 mole of Cu and 1 mole of H_2 by electrolysis requires twice this quantity, i.e. 2×96500 C.

This experiment shows that the production of one mole of an element from its ion by electrolysis requires $n \times 96500$ coulombs, where 'n' is the number of electrons in the relevant ion-electron equation.

We can extend the same principle to industrial situations, such as

(i) nickel-plating: 1 mole of nickel atoms will be produced from 1 mole of Ni^{2+} by using 2×96500 C,

(ii) electrolysis of molten aluminium oxide: 1 mole of Al atoms will be produced from 1 mole of Al^{3+} by using 3×96500 C.

A similar situation occurs at the positive electrodes in the cells in figure 1. The relevant ion-electron equation are as shown on the next page.

51

Cell C: $2Cl^- \rightarrow Cl_2 + 2e^-$

Cells A and B: $2H_2O \rightarrow O_2 + 4H^+ + 4e^-$
(or $4OH^- \rightarrow O_2 + 2H_2O + 4e^-$)

Thus, the production of 1 mole of Cl_2 molecules from 2 moles of Cl^- needs 2×96500 C, and 1 mole of O_2 molecules from 2 moles of H_2O (or 4 moles of OH^-) needs 4×96500 C.

Let us now go back to consider the reaction occurring at the negative electrode in cell A.

$$Ag^+ + e^- \rightarrow Ag$$

According to this equation each atom of silver is the result of a silver ion gaining one electron. This means that the production of one mole of silver, which contains the Avogadro Constant of atoms, (i.e. L atoms of silver), requires one mole of silver ions gaining one mole of electrons.

As shown above, the quantity of electricity needed to achieve this is 96500 coulombs. In other words, 96500 coulombs is the total charge of one mole of electrons.

This enables us to calculate a value for the Avogadro Constant provided that the charge of one electron is known. This can be determined by what is commonly referred to as Millikan's oil drop experiment in which charged oil droplets are suspended between charged plates. Further details of this important experiment may be obtained from a suitable Physics textbook. The charge of one electron is found to be 1.60×10^{-19}C.

Hence, the Avogadro Constant, L

$$= \frac{\text{total charge of 1 mole of electrons}}{\text{charge of 1 electron}}$$

$$= \frac{96500 \text{ C mol}^{-1}}{1.6 \times 10^{-19}\text{C}}$$

$$= 6.03 \times 10^{23} \text{ mol}^{-1}$$

This is just one of several methods by which the Avogadro Constant can be determined. The accepted value for the Avogadro Constant is 6.02×10^{23} mol^{-1}, i.e. more than six hundred thousand million million million!

Let us now apply this to some of the examples discussed in the previous section, pages 49 and 50.

a) Metals and monatomic species

4 g of helium
27 g of aluminium } each contain 6.02×10^{23} atoms.
197 g of gold

b) Covalent substances – see table 5.

Quantity of substance	Number of molecules	Number of atoms
2 g H_2	6.02×10^{23} (L)	1.204×10^{24} (2L)
18 g H_2O	6.02×10^{23} (L)	1.806×10^{24} (3L)
30 g C_2H_6	6.02×10^{23} (L)	4.816×10^{24} (8L) comprising 1.204×10^{24} C atoms (2L) 3.612×10^{24} H atoms (6L)

Table 5

c) Ionic Compounds – see table 6.

Quantity of substance	Number of positive ions	Number of negative ions	Total number of ions
58.5 g Na^+Cl^-	6.02×10^{23} Na^+	6.02×10^{23} Cl^-	1.204×10^{24} (2L)
148 g $Mg^{2+}(NO_3^-)_2$	6.02×10^{23} Mg^{2+}	1.204×10^{24} NO_3^-	1.806×10^{24} (3L)
342 g $(Al^{3+})_2(SO_4^{2-})_3$	1.204×10^{24} Al^{3+}	1.806×10^{24} SO_4^{2-}	3.01×10^{24} (5L)

Table 6

CALCULATIONS INVOLVING QUANTITATIVE ELECTROLYSIS

It is possible to calculate the mass of electrode product during electrolysis provided that

(i) the ion-electron equation for the reaction occurring at the electrode is known,

(ii) sufficient information is given to enable the quantity of electricity to be calculated, using the relationship:

Quantity of electricity = Current × Time
(in coulombs)　(in amps)　(in seconds)

Alternatively if the mass of electrode product is known, the quantity of electricity can be calculated. From this, either the current or the time during which electrolysis has occurred can be found provided the other quantity is known.

Worked example 3.1

Copper(II) chloride solution was electrolysed for 64 minutes 20 seconds using a current of 0.5 A. Calculate the mass of product at each electrode.

Current = 0.5 A   Time = 3860 s
Quantity of electricity   = Current × Time
$$= 0.5 \times 3860$$
$$= 1930 \, C$$

(a) The product at the negative electrode (cathode) is copper.

$$\text{Equation: } Cu^{2+} + 2e^- \rightarrow Cu$$

According to this equation,

2 moles of electrons (i.e. $2 \times 96500 \, C$) are

needed to produce 1 mole of Cu (i.e. 64 g)

i.e. 193000 C produce 64 g Cu
Hence 1930 C produce 0.64 g Cu.

(b) The product at the positive electrode (anode) is chlorine.

$$\text{Equation: } 2Cl^- \rightarrow Cl_2 + 2e^-$$

According to this equation,

2 moles of electrons (i.e. $2 \times 96500 \, C$) are involved in producing 1 mole of Cl_2 (i.e. 71 g)

i.e. 193000 C produce 71 g Cl_2
Hence 1930 C produce 0.71 g Cl_2.

CALCULATIONS USING THE AVOGADRO CONSTANT

When carrying out calculations involving the Avogadro Constant, it is important to be aware of the chemical nature of the substance. Clear thinking is essential to avoid confusing atoms and molecules or atoms and ions. Two worked examples follow.

Worked example 3.2

Calculate the number of molecules in 6.4 g of methane and hence find the total number of atoms present.

Methane is CH_4.
Molecular mass = 16.

Number of moles of methane molecules $= \dfrac{6.4}{16}$
$$= 0.4$$

Number of methane molecules
$$= 0.4 \times L$$
$$= 0.4 \times 6.02 \times 10^{23}$$
$$= 2.408 \times 10^{23}$$

Each molecule contains 5 atoms (1 of carbon, 4 of hydrogen).
Hence total number of atoms
$$= 5 \times 0.4 \times L$$
$$= 5 \times 0.4 \times 6.02 \times 10^{23}$$
$$= 1.204 \times 10^{24}$$

Worked example 3.3

Calculate the number of metal ions present in $100 \, cm^3$ 2 M sodium carbonate solution and also find the total number of ions.

Sodium carbonate is Na_2CO_3 or $(Na^+)_2 \, CO_3^{2-}$. i.e. the 'formula-unit' contains two Na^+ ions and one CO_3^{2-} ion.

Number of moles of sodium carbonate present,

$$n = C \times V$$
$$= 2 \times \frac{100}{1000}$$
$$= 0.2$$

Number of Na^+ ions present $= 2 \times 0.2 \times L$
$$= 2.408 \times 10^{23}$$
Total number of ions present $= 3 \times 0.2 \times L$
$$= 3.612 \times 10^{23}$$

MOLAR VOLUME OF GASES

We have seen how we can relate a mole of a substance to an actual mass. When dealing with a gas, however, it is often more useful to measure quantity in volume. In table 7 several gases are compared. The molar volume of each gas at 0°C and one atmosphere pressure is calculated by dividing its molar mass by its density at that temperature and pressure.

$$density = \frac{mass}{volume} \quad so \ that: \quad volume = \frac{mass}{density}$$

Gas:	H_2	CH_4	N_2	O_2	Ar	CO_2
Mass of 1 mole/g	2	16	28	32	40	44
Density at 0°C and 1 at. pr./g l^{-1}	0.09	0.71	1.25	1.43	1.78	1.98
Volume of 1 mole at 0°C and 1 at. pr./l	22.2	22.2	22.4	22.4	22.5	22.2
(at.pr. = atmospheric pressure)						

Table 7

When comparing different gases we can see that while the molar masses differ in value so also in proportion do their densities. Consequently when the molar volumes of different gases are calculated, we observe that the value, within certain limits, is the same for all gases at the same temperature and pressure.

This can be tested experimentally as follows. A round-bottomed flask can be evacuated and then weighed. It can be reweighed after filling with a gas. This can be repeated using other gases. The volume can then be calculated from the data obtained as illustrated in worked example 3.4 below.

Instead of evacuating it, the flask can be weighed with air in it. The density of air under experimental conditions of temperature and pressure can be obtained from a suitable data book. Once the volume of the flask is known the mass of air in it can be calculated and hence the mass of the empty flask can be found.

Worked example 3.4

Mass of empty flask $= 107.49$ g
Volume of flask $= 480 \text{ cm}^3$
Mass of flask + carbon dioxide $= 108.37$ g
(All measurements made 20°C and at 1 atmosphere pressure.)

Use the data given above to calculate the molar volume of carbon dioxide.

Mass of carbon dioxide $= 0.88$ g
0.88 g of carbon dioxide has a volume of 480 cm³ at 20°C and 1 atmosphere pressure.
Hence, 1 mole (44 g) of CO_2 has a volume of

$$480 \times \frac{44}{0.88} = 24000 \text{ cm}^3$$

Hence, molar volume of CO_2 is 24.0 litres, at 20°C and 1 atmosphere pressure.

When quoting a value for the molar volume of a gas the temperature and pressure ought to be specified. At 20°C or 293 K and 1 atmosphere pressure the molar volume of any gas is just over 24 litres per mole (1 mol^{-1}).

It may seem surprising at first that the molar volume is the same for all gases even at the same temperature and pressure. This is certainly not true for either solids or liquids. In a gas, however, the molecules have much greater kinetic energy and are relatively far apart so that the volume does not depend on the size of the actual molecules. It is possible to calculate that in a gas at room temperature and pressure the molecules themselves only occupy about 0.1% of the volume of the gas. The rest is empty space!

CALCULATIONS INVOLVING VOLUMES OF GASES

Since all gases have the same molar volume, it follows that equal volumes of different gases at the same temperature and pressure will contain the same number of moles and, consequently, the same number of molecules. Thus, one litre of oxygen contains the same number of moles (and also molecules) as one litre of methane at the same temperature and pressure.

If the molar volume of a gas at 20°C and 1 atmosphere pressure is 24 1 mol^{-1}, then, for example

1.2 litres contain 0.05 mol, or 3.01×10^{22} molecules;
96 litres contain 4 mol, or 2.408×10^{24} molecules;
0.2 mol occupy 4.8 litres; 5 mol occupy 120 litres.

Furthermore in a chemical reaction which involves gases we can relate the volumes of the gases to the number of moles as expressed in the equation for the reaction, always provided that the temperature and pressure are constant.

Let us consider the reaction in which carbon monoxide and oxygen combine to form carbon dioxide.

$$2CO(g) + O_2(g) \rightarrow 2CO_2(g)$$

According to the equation, 2 moles of carbon monoxide combine with one mole of oxygen to form 2 moles of carbon dioxide. Consequently, at the same temperature and pressure, any volume of carbon monoxide will produce the same volume of carbon dioxide by reacting with half that volume of oxygen.

Thus, 2 litres CO + 1 litre O_2 gives 2 litres CO_2
and 100 cm^3 CO + 50 cm^3 O_2 gives 100 cm^3 CO_2.

Worked example 3.5

Calculate the volume of oxygen required for the complete combustion of 1 litre of ethane and also the volume of each product. All volumes are measured at 150°C and 1 atmosphere pressure.

$$2C_2H_6(g) + 7O_2(g) \rightarrow 4CO_2(g) + 6H_2O(g)$$

Mole ratio of reactants and products	2	7	4	6
Volume ratio of reactants and products (at same T and P)	2	7	4	6
i.e.	1	3.5	2	3

Hence, 1 litre of ethane requires 3.5 litres of oxygen for complete combustion and produces 2 litres of $CO_2(g)$ and 3 litres of $H_2O(g)$.

In many reactions which involve gases one or more of the reactants or products may be a liquid or a solid. When this is the case the volume is so small when compared with that of the gas or gases that it can be regarded as negligible.

Thus if the reaction in the previous worked example is carried out when all volumes are measured at room temperature and pressure, the products are carbon dioxide and water. The latter, being a liquid, has negligible volume by comparison.

$$2C_2H_6(g) + 7O_2(g) \rightarrow 4CO_2(g) + 6H_2O(l)$$

Mole ratio:	2	7	4	6
Volume ratio:	2	7	4	negligible
i.e.	1	3.5	2	—

Thus 1 litre of ethane requires 3.5 litres of oxygen for complete combustion and produces 2 litres of carbon dioxide when the volumes are measured at room temperature and pressure. Incidentally, the volume of water formed would be about 2 cm^3, less than 0.1% of the volume calculated in worked example 3.5.

Worked example 3.6

20 cm^3 of propane was completely burned. Calculate the volume of oxygen required and the volume of gaseous product. All volumes are measured under the same conditions of room temperature and pressure.

Equation:	$C_3H_8(g)$	$+ 5O_2(g) \rightarrow$	$3CO_2(g) +$	$4H_2O(l)$
Mole ratio:	1	5	3	4
Volume ratio:	1	5	3	negligible

Hence, 20 cm^3 of propane will require (5 × 20) i.e. 100 cm^3 of oxygen.
and will produce (3 × 20) i.e. 60 cm^3 of carbon dioxide.

From previous work you should know how to use balanced equations to calculate the mass of a reactant or product in a reaction. This can now be extended to include calculation of a volume in reactions where a gas or gases are involved. This is illustrated in the following worked example.

Worked example 3.7

Calculate the volume of carbon dioxide released when 0.4 g of calcium carbonate is dissolved in excess hydrochloric acid. The gas is collected at room temperature and pressure. It has a density of 1.83 g l^{-1} under these conditions.

1 mole of CO_2 weighs 44 g

Molar volume of $CO_2 = \dfrac{\text{mass}}{\text{density}} = \dfrac{44}{1.83} = 24 \text{ l}$

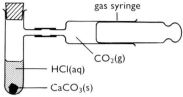

Equation: $CaCO_3(s) + 2HCl(aq) \rightarrow CaCl_2(aq) + CO_2(g) + H_2O(l)$

From the equation, 1 mole of $CaCO_3$ (100 g) gives 1 mole of CO_2 (24 l).

Figure 2

Number of moles of $CaCO_3 = \dfrac{0.4}{100} = 0.004$

Hence, 0.004 moles of CO_2 formed.
Volume of CO_2 formed $= 0.004 \times 24 \text{ l} = 0.096 \text{ l or } 96 \text{ cm}^3$

This result could be tested experimentally using an apparatus like that shown in figure 2. Alternatively, the gas could be collected over water in a measuring cylinder.

CALCULATIONS TO IDENTIFY REACTANTS IN EXCESS

In previous calculations based on equations it has usually been indicated or at least assumed that one of the reactants is present in excess and as a result the calculation is based on the mass or volume of the other reactant or of a product. A further degree of difficulty can be introduced if the amounts of both reactants are known and you are then expected to find out which one is in excess.

This is illustrated by the following two worked examples. They are essentially modifications of examples 3.6 and 3.7 in the previous section.

Worked example 3.8

A mixture of 20 cm³ of propane and 130 cm³ of oxygen was ignited and allowed to cool. Calculate the volume and composition of the residual gaseous mixture, provided that all the volumes are measured under the same conditions of room temperature and pressure.

Equation:	$C_3H_8(g)$	+ $5O_2(g)$	$\rightarrow 3CO_2(g)$	+ $4H_2O(l)$
Mole ratio:	1	5	3	4
Volume ratio:	1	5	3	negligible

According to the equation, 20 cm^3 of propane requires (5 × 20) i.e. 100 cm^3 of oxygen.
Hence, oxygen is present in excess as its initial volume is 130 cm^3.
The rest of the calculation should be based on the quantity of the other reactant, i.e. propane, since there is more than enough oxygen for complete combustion.

Volume of excess oxygen = (130 − 100) = 30 cm^3
Volume of carbon dioxide formed = (3 × 20) = 60 cm^3

Hence, the residual gaseous mixture consists of 30 cm^3 of O_2 and 60 cm^3 of CO_2.

Worked example 3.9

Calculate the volume of carbon dioxide released when 0.5 g of calcium carbonate is added to 10 cm^3 0.5 M (0.5 mol l^{-1}) hydrochloric acid. The gas is collected at room temperature and pressure and its molar volume is 24 l mol^{-1} under these conditions.

Equation: $CaCO_3(g) + 2HCl(aq) \rightarrow CaCl_2(aq) + CO_2(g) + H_2O(l)$

Mole ratio: 1   2   1

Since the amounts of both reactants are given it is necessary first of all to determine which one is present in excess.

Number of moles of $CaCO_3$ $= \dfrac{0.5}{100} = 0.005$

Number of moles of HCl $=$ Concentration × Volume (in litres) $= 0.5 \times \dfrac{10}{1000} = 0.005$

According to the equation,   1 mole of $CaCO_3$ requires 2 moles of HCl,
and hence,   0.005 moles $CaCO_3$ require 0.01 moles of HCl.

As there is less than this amount of acid present, not all of the calcium carbonate will react, i.e. it is present in excess. Consequently the volume of CO_2 released will depend on the amount of acid present.

According to the equation,   2 moles of HCl will release 1 mole of CO_2,
and hence,   0.005 moles of HCl will release 0.0025 moles of CO_2

Hence, the volume of CO_2

$= 0.0025 \times 24$ l
$= 0.006$ l or 60 cm^3

This could be verified by modifying the experiment referred to on page 59, figure 2. As well as measuring the volume of gas, the excess calcium carbonate could be recovered by filtration, washed and dried before weighing.

CALCULATION OF PERCENTAGE YIELD

Balanced equations enable us to calculate the quantity of product which could be obtained from a known amount of reactant, assuming that 100% conversion takes place. The quantity of product thus calculated is known as the *theoretical yield*.

The *actual yield* obtained is usually less than the theoretical yield. A variety of reasons could account for this, such as the reaction not going to completion or other reactions occurring which 'compete' with the main reaction. Separation of the desired product may be difficult or the product may be impure and some of it lost during purification. You will appreciate that poor practical technique is likely to have a drastic effect on the actual yield.

In industrial processes a high percentage yield as well as high purity of product is desirable. Where this is not possible or economically feasible, unconverted reactants are frequently recycled for further reaction, for example, in the Haber process to make ammonia.

The percentage yield of product can be derived from the following relationship.

$$\text{percentage yield} = \frac{\text{actual yield}}{\text{theoretical yield}} \times 100\%$$

Worked example 3.10

A sample of calcium carbonate weighing 2 g was heated strongly for several minutes and 420 cm^3 of carbon dioxide was collected over water. Taking the molar volume to be 24 l mol^{-1} under experimental conditions, calculate the percentage yield of the gas.

Equation: $CaCO_3(g) \rightarrow CaO(s) + CO_2(g)$

According to the equation, 1 mole of $CaCO_3$ should yield 1 mole of CO_2
(100 g) (24 l)

Hence, 2 g of $CaCO_3$ should yield 0.48 l of CO_2
i.e. the theoretical yield is 480 cm^3.

Hence, the percentage yield $= \dfrac{420}{480} \times 100 = 87.5\%$

REDOX REACTIONS

Reactions in which reduction and oxidation occur are called REDOX reactions. In a redox reaction electron transfer occurs between the reactants. One reactant is reduced while the other is oxidised. Table 8 summarises important definitions and gives examples of ion-electron equations. It also emphasises the mnemonic, OILRIG, to help you remember that oxidation involves electron loss and reduction involves electron gain.

When a **reducing agent** reacts it loses electrons and, as a result, is itself **oxidised.**	When an **oxidising agent** reacts it gains electrons and, as a result, is itself **reduced**.
e.g. $Mg \rightarrow Mg^{2+} + 2e^-$	e.g. $Cu^{2+} + 2e^- \rightarrow Cu$
$Zn \rightarrow Zn^{2+} + 2e^-$	$Ag^+ + e^- \rightarrow Ag$
OXIDATION **IS** **L**OSS of electrons	**R**EDUCTION **IS** **G**AIN of electrons

'OILRIG'

Table 8

In earlier work you will have come across a type of reaction called *displacement* in which one metal displaces another metal from a solution of its salt. This happens when the metal added has a greater tendency to lose electrons and form ions than the metal being displaced. In other words, the atoms of the metal added lose electrons to the ions of the metal being displaced from solution. The relevant ion-electron equations can be combined to produce a balanced ionic equation for the overall redox reaction as illustrated by the following two examples.

a) *Magnesium displaces copper from a solution containing copper(II) ions.*

The following ion-electron equations show that each magnesium atom loses 2 electrons to a copper(II) ion. Since the same number of electrons is lost and gained, the ion-electron equations can be added as follows to give a balanced ionic equation for the redox reaction. Note that the redox equation does *not* contain electrons.

Oxidation: $\qquad\qquad Mg(s) \rightarrow Mg^{2+}(aq) + 2e^-$
Reduction: $Cu^{2+}(aq) + 2e^- \rightarrow Cu(s)$

_____

Redox: $\quad Cu^{2+}(aq) + Mg(s) \rightarrow Cu(s) + Mg^{2+}(aq)$

b) *Zinc displaces silver from a solution containing silver(I) ions.*

In this example the ion-electron equations show that each zinc atom loses 2 electrons while each silver ion gains only 1 electron. Therefore, the second ion-electron equation must be doubled to balance the number of electrons lost and gained, so that the redox equation can be obtained in the same way as in the previous example. Note that the total charge on each side of the redox equation is the same.

Oxidation: $\qquad\qquad Zn(s) \rightarrow Zn^{2+}(aq) + 2e^-$
Reduction: $\quad Ag^+(aq) + e^- \rightarrow Ag(s) \qquad\qquad (\times 2)$

_____

Redox: $\quad 2Ag^+(aq) + Zn(s) \rightarrow 2Ag(s) + Zn^{2+}(aq)$

In each of the above examples the negative ions present in the solutions have not been included or even referred to since they do not take part in the reaction. It is usual practice to omit *spectator ions* from redox equations.

So far we have dealt with relatively simple ion-electron equations which involve simple ions and atoms or molecules. Equations involving *oxyanions* are more complex. Oxyanions are negative ions which contain oxygen combined with another element, for example, sulphite ions (SO_3^{2-}) and permanganate ions (MnO_4^-).

The following three examples of redox reactions are given to emphasise two main points, namely

(i) to show how to write ion-electron equations which involve oxyanions, and

(ii) to illustrate further the writing of balanced redox equations.

State symbols have been omitted so as not to 'overload' the equations with information.

(1) Bromine water, $Br_2(aq)$ + Sodium sulphite solution, $Na_2SO_3(aq)$
     (Oxidising agent)   (Reducing agent)
                                Spectator ions: Na^+

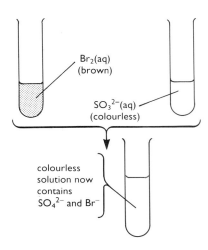

Test for sulphate ions: adding barium chloride solution forms white precipitate of $BaSO_4$, insoluble in dilute HCl

Figure 3

Bromine molecules are reduced to bromine ions.

$$Br_2 + 2e^- \rightarrow 2Br^-$$
$$\text{brown} \qquad\qquad \text{colourless}$$

Sulphite ions are oxidised to sulphate ions. Both ions are colourless (figure 3).

$$SO_3^{2-} \rightarrow SO_4^{2-}$$

To complete the ion-electron equation for this change, firstly add H_2O to the left-hand side and $2H^+$ to the right-hand side to give

$$SO_4^{2-} + H_2O \rightarrow SO_4^{2-} + 2H^+$$

and secondly add two electrons to the right-hand side so that the charge is the same on each side of the equation giving

$$SO_3^{2-} + H_2O \rightarrow SO_4^{2-} + 2H^+ + 2e^-$$

The two ion-electron equations can now be combined to give the balanced redox equation as follows.

$$Br_2 + 2e^- \rightarrow 2Br^-$$
$$SO_3^{2-} + H_2O \rightarrow SO_4^{2-} + 2H^+ + 2e^-$$
$$\overline{Br_2 + SO_3^{2-} + H_2O \rightarrow 2Br^- + SO_4^{2-} + 2H^+}$$

(2) Acidified potassium permanganate solution, $KMnO_4(aq) + H^+(aq)$ (Oxidising agent) + Iron(II) sulphate solution, $FeSO_4(aq)$ (Reducing agent)

Spectator ions: K^+, SO_4^{2-}

Iron(II) ions are oxidised to iron(III) ions (figure 4).

$$Fe^{2+} \rightarrow Fe^{3+} + e^-$$

Permanganate ions are reduced to manganese(II) ions.

$$MnO_4^- \rightarrow Mn^{2+}$$
$$\text{purple} \qquad \text{colourless}$$

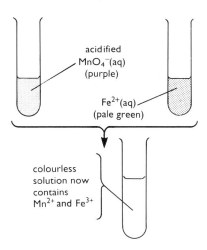

Test for iron (III) ions: adding ammonium thiocyanate gives a dark blood red solution

Figure 4

The ion-electron equation can be completed in a similar way to the example above. Only this time oxygen is being removed so that $4H_2O$ is added to the right-hand side and

$8H^+$ to the left to give

$$MnO_4^- + 8H^+ \rightarrow Mn^{2+} + 4H_2O$$

Five electrons are then added to the left-hand side to balance the charge giving

$$MnO_4^- + 8H^+ + 5e^- \rightarrow Mn^{2+} + 4H_2O$$

This equation shows why the solution should be acidified.

The two ion-electron equations can now be combined to give the balanced redox equation. To balance number of electrons lost and gained, the equation involving iron ions has to be multiplied by 5.

$$5Fe^{2+} \rightarrow 5Fe^{3+} + 5e^-$$
$$MnO_4^- + 8H^+ + 5e^- \rightarrow Mn^{2+} + 4H_2O$$
$$\overline{MnO_4^- + 8H^+ + 5Fe^{2+} \rightarrow Mn^{2+} + 5Fe^{3+} + 4H_2O}$$

(3) Dilute nitric acid, $HNO_3(aq)$ + Copper, $Cu(s)$
   (Oxidising agent)   (Reducing agent)

Copper atoms are oxidised to copper(II) ions.

$$Cu \rightarrow Cu^{2+} + 2e^-$$

Nitrate ions are reduced to nitrogen monoxide, NO, a colourless gas which forms brown fumes of nitrogen dioxide in contact with air (figure 5).

$$NO_3^- \rightarrow NO$$

Two oxygen atoms are being removed, so add $2H_2O$ to the right-hand side and $4H^+$ to the left.

$$NO_3^- + 4H^+ \rightarrow NO + 2H_2O$$

Finally three electrons are needed on the left-hand side to balance the charge.

$$NO_3^- + 4H^+ + 3e^- \rightarrow NO + 2H_2O$$

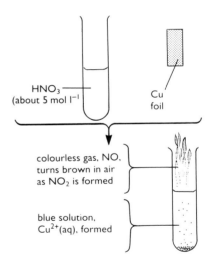

HNO₃ (about 5 mol l⁻¹)

Cu foil

colourless gas, NO, turns brown in air as NO₂ is formed

blue solution, Cu^{2+}(aq), formed

Figure 5

In order to write the balanced redox equation it is necessary to multiply the equation involving copper by 3 and the equation involving nitrate ions by 2.

$$3\,Cu \rightarrow 3\,Cu^{2+} + 6\,e^-$$
$$2\,NO_3^- + 8\,H^+ + 6\,e^- \rightarrow 2\,NO + 4\,H_2O$$
$$\overline{3\,Cu + 2\,NO_3^- + 8\,H^+ \rightarrow 3\,Cu^{2+} + 2\,NO + 4\,H_2O}$$

In most data books ion–electron equations are listed as reductions on a table known as the *Electrochemical series*. In other words, the equations are written in the form:

$$\text{oxidising agent} + \text{electron(s)} \rightarrow \text{reducing agent}$$

When using equations from this series to write a redox equation it will always be necessary to reverse one of the equations as it appears on the table, since an oxidising agent can only react with a reducing agent and vice versa. This is illustrated by the following examples.

(1) Iron(III) chloride solution oxidises potassium iodide solution to form iodine. (Cl^- and K^+ are spectator ions.) The relevant ion–electron equations from the electrochemical series are:

$$I_2 + 2\,e^- \rightarrow 2\,I^-$$
$$Fe^{3+} + e^- \rightarrow Fe^{2+}$$

Since the iodide ions are oxidised the first equation must be reversed. The equation for the reduction of iron(III) ions must be doubled to balance the number of electrons transferred.

$$2\,I^- \rightarrow I_2 + 2\,e^-$$
$$2\,Fe^{3+} + 2\,e^- \rightarrow 2\,Fe^{2+}$$
$$\overline{2\,Fe^{3+} + 2\,I^- \rightarrow 2\,Fe^{2+} + I_2}$$

(2) Iron(II) sulphate solution reduces potassium dichromate solution to form chromium(III) ions. (SO_4^{2-} and K^+ are spectator ions.) The relevant ion–electron equations from the electrochemical series are:

$$Fe^{3+} + e^- \rightarrow Fe^{2+}$$
$$Cr_2O_7^{2-} + 14\,H^+ + 6\,e^- \rightarrow 2\,Cr^{3+} + 7\,H_2O$$

The first equation must be reversed and multiplied by 6 to balance the number of electrons transferred.

$$6Fe^{2+} \rightarrow 6Fe^{3+} + 6e^-$$
$$Cr_2O_7^{2-} + 14H^+ + 6e^- \rightarrow 2Cr^{3+} + 7H_2O$$
$$\overline{Cr_2O_7^{2-} + 14H^+ + 6Fe^{2+} \rightarrow 6Fe^{3+} + 2Cr^{3+} + 7H_2O}$$

REDOX TITRATIONS

In previous work you will have carried out volumetric titrations involving acids and alkalis in which, for example, a fixed volume of alkali contained in a conical flask is titrated with an acid of known concentration contained in a burette. The volume of acid required to neutralise the alkali is found, a suitable indicator being used to determine the end-point of the titration. The balanced equation for the reaction is then used in calculating the concentration of the alkali.

Volumetric analysis, as this procedure is also known, can be applied to redox reactions. For example, the concentration of a solution of a reducing agent can be determined using a solution of a suitable oxidising agent of known concentration provided that

(i) the balanced redox equation is known or can be derived from the relevant ion-electron equations,

(ii) the volumes of the reactants are accurately measured by pipette and burette, and

(iii) some method of indicating the end-point of the titration is available.

Two examples of redox titrations are given below. A brief outline of the experimental procedure is followed by a specimen calculation to show how the concentration of an aqueous solution of a reducing agent or an oxidising agent may be calculated from the results obtained.

Example 1

To determine the concentration of an iron(II) sulphate solution by titration with a potassium permanganate solution of known concentration.

Experimental procedure (figure 6):
20 cm^3 of iron(II) sulphate solution is transferred by pipette to a conical flask and excess dilute sulphuric acid is added. Potassium permanganate solution (0.02 mol 1^{-1}) is added from the burette until the contents of the flask just turn from colourless to purple, initial and final burette readings being noted. The titration is repeated a few times to obtain 3 concordant titres, i.e. within ± 0.1 cm^3.

Since the permanganate solution is so strongly coloured compared to the other solutions the reaction is self-indicating and the change at the end-point from colourless to purple is quite sharp.

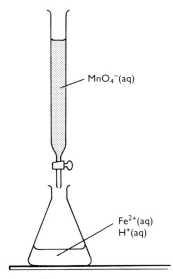

Figure 6

A specimen calculation is given in worked example 3.11.

Worked example 3.11

Specimen calculation:

Calculate the concentration of an iron(II) sulphate solution given that 20.0 cm^3 of it reacted with 24.0 cm^3 of 0.02 M ($0.02 \text{ mol } l^{-1}$) potassium permanganate solution.

$$MnO_4^- + 8H^+ + 5Fe^{2+} \rightarrow 5Fe^{3+} + Mn^{2+} + 4H_2O$$

According to the equation, 1 mole of MnO_4^- oxidises 5 moles of Fe^{2+}.

Number of moles of MnO_4^- used $\quad = $ Concentration $(\text{mol } l^{-1}) \times$ Volume(l)

$$= 0.02 \times \frac{24}{1000} = 4.8 \times 10^{-4}$$

Hence, number of moles of $Fe^{2+}(aq)$ present $= 5 \times 4.8 \times 10^{-4} = 2.4 \times 10^{-3}$

This is contained in 20 cm^3, i.e. 0.02 litres.

Hence, concentration of $Fe^{2+}(aq) \quad = \dfrac{\text{Number of moles}}{\text{Volume (l)}} = \dfrac{2.4 \times 10^{-3}}{0.02} = 0.12 \text{ mol } l^{-1}$

Since 1 mole $FeSO_4(aq)$ contains 1 mole of $Fe^{2+}(aq)$, concentration of $FeSO_4(aq)$
$$= 0.12 \text{ mol } l^{-1} \text{ or } 0.12 \text{ M}$$

Alternatively, the concentration of iron(II) sulphate solution can be found by using the following relationship.

Concentration $\times$ volume $\times$ number of electrons gained per mole of Oxidising Agent	$=$	Concentration $\times$ volume $\times$ number of electrons lost per mole of Reducing Agent

The two concentrations must be in the same units, i.e. $\text{mol } l^{-1}$, and the two volumes must also be expressed in the same units but do not have to be changed into litres, i.e. they can be in cubic centimetres or litres.

Let us now apply this relationship to the above example.

Oxidising Agent (MnO_4^-): concentration $\times$ volume $\times$ number of e^- gained	$=$	Reducing Agent (Fe^{2+}): concentration $\times$ volume $\times$ number of e^- lost
$0.02 \times 24 \times 5$	$= ? \times 20 \times 1$	

Hence, concentration of $Fe^{2+}(aq) \quad = \dfrac{0.02 \times 24 \times 5}{20 \times 1} = 0.12 \text{ mol } l^{-1}$

Using a relationship like the one above probably makes it easier to obtain the correct answer! However, ability to use it does not mean that you understand why it applies. Try to work out why it does by comparison with the previous method of calculation.

Example 2

To determine the concentration of an iodine solution by titration with a sodium thiosulphate solution of known concentration.

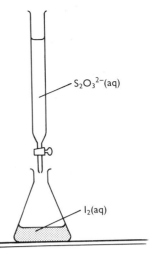

Experimental procedure (figure 7):
20 cm³ of iodine solution is transferred by pipette to a conical flask. Sodium thiosulphate solution ($0.2 \text{ mol } 1^{-1}$) is added from the burette until the iodine solution turns from red to pale yellow. A few drops of starch solution are added as indicator and the titration continued until the blue colour just disappears. Initial and final burette readings are noted and the titration is repeated a few times to obtain 3 concordant titres.

A specimen calculation is given in worked example 3.12.

Figure 7

Worked example 3.12

20 cm³ of an iodine solution required 18.0 cm³ of 0.2 M ($0.2 \text{ mol } 1^{-1}$) sodium thiosulphate solution for complete reaction. Calculate the concentration of the iodine solution.

$$I_2 \quad + \quad 2e^- \quad \rightarrow 2I^-$$

$$2S_2O_3^{2-} \quad \rightarrow S_4O_6^{2-} + \quad 2e^-$$

$$I_2 \quad + \quad 2S_2O_3^{2-} \rightarrow 2I^- \quad + \quad S_4O_6^{2-}$$

According to the equation, 1 mole of I_2 is reduced by 2 moles of $S_2O_3^{2-}$.

Number of moles of $S_2O_3^{2-}$ used $= 0.2 \times \dfrac{18}{1000} \quad = 3.6 \times 10^{-3}$

Hence, number of moles of I_2 present $= 0.5 \times 3.6 \times 10^{-3} \quad = 1.8 \times 10^{-3}$

This is contained in 20 cm³, i.e. 0.02 litres.

Hence, concentration of I_2(aq) $= \dfrac{1.8 \times 10^{-3}}{0.02} \quad = 0.09 \text{ mol } 1^{-1} \text{ or } 0.09 \text{ M}$

Alternatively:

Oxidising Agent (I_2):
concentration × volume × number of
e^- gained

$=$

Reducing Agent ($S_2O_3^{2-}$):
concentration × volume × number of
e^- lost

$? \times 20 \times 2 \qquad = 0.2 \times 18 \times 1$

Hence, concentration of I_2(aq) $= \dfrac{0.02 \times 18 \times 1}{20 \times 2} \quad = 0.09 \text{ mol } 1^{-1}$

Examples for practice

SECTION A: Revision of Standard Grade aspects of the mole.

$$\text{Number of moles in a given mass} = \frac{\text{given mass (g)}}{\text{mass of 1 mole (g)}}$$

1. Calculate the number of moles in
   (a) 40 g of neon gas
   (b) 8 g of oxygen gas
   (c) 13.2 g of ammonium sulphate
   (d) 2 kg of hydrated copper (II) sulphate, $CuSO_4.5H_2O$. (8)

2. Calculate the percentage of carbon in each of the following compounds
   (a) Ethanol. C_2H_5OH
   (b) Sucrose, $C_{12}H_{22}O_{11}$
   (c) Trichloromethane, $CHCl_3$
   (d) Aluminium carbonate, $Al_2(CO_3)_3$. (8)

3. Calculate (i) the number of moles, and (ii) the mass of solute in each of the following solutions:
   (a) 100 cm³ of 0.2 mol l⁻¹ $AgNO_3$
   (b) 1.5 litres of 4 mol l⁻¹ Na_2CO_3
   (c) 250 cm³ of 2 M $Mg(NO_3)_2$
   (d) 5 litres of 0.5 M $(NH_4)_2SO_4$. (8)

4. Calculate the empirical formula of each of the following compounds from the data given.
   (a) 2.8 g of hydrocarbon A contains 2.4 g of carbon.
   (b) 6.3 g of compound B contains sodium, 1.6 g of sulphur and 2.4 g of oxygen.
   (c) Percentage composition by mass of compound C: 62.5% Pb, 8.5% N, 29% O.
   (d) Percentage composition by mass of compound D: 40% C, 6.7% H, 53.3% O. (8)

   Compound A has a molecular mass of 42 and compound D has a molecular mass of 180. Use this information and their empirical formulae to derive the molecular formulae of A and D. (2)
   (Total: 10)

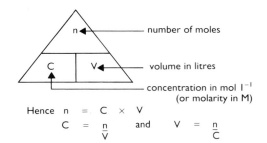

Hence $n = C \times V$
$C = \dfrac{n}{V}$ and $V = \dfrac{n}{C}$

5. Calculate the concentration in mol l⁻¹ of each of the following solutions.
   (a) 0.3 moles of NaCl in 600 cm³ of solution (1)
   (b) 5 moles of KNO_3 in 2 litres of solution (1)
   (c) 3.31 g of $Pb(NO_3)_2$ in 200 cm³ of solution (2)
   (d) 1 kg of NaOH in 5 litres of solution. (2)
   (Total: 6)

6. In each of the following examples (i) where necessary, balance the equation, and (ii) calculate the required quantity.
   (a) $CuCO_3 + H_2SO_4$
       $\rightarrow CuSO_4 + CO_2 + H_2O$
   What mass of copper(II) sulphate would be obtained on adding 6.2 g of copper(II) carbonate to an excess of dilute sulphuric acid? (2)
   (b) $Fe_2O_3 + CO \rightarrow Fe + CO_2$
   What mass of iron(III) oxide is needed to yield 14 kg of iron on complete reduction? (3)
   (c) $CaCl_2(aq) + AgNO_3(aq)$
       $\rightarrow AgCl(s) + Ca(NO_3)_2(aq)$
   What mass of calcium chloride is needed to precipitate 14.35 g of silver(I) chloride from an excess of silver(I) nitrate solution? (3)
   (Total: 8)

7. In each of the following examples, write a balanced equation for the reaction and use it to calculate the concentration, in mol l^{-1}, of the solution in italics.
(a) 20 cm^3 of 2 mol l^{-1} KOH(aq) neutralises 16.0 cm^3 of *HNO$_3$(aq)*.   (3)
(b) 20.0 cm^3 of *Na$_2$CO$_3$(aq)* neutralises 25.0 cm^3 of 0.8 mol l^{-1} HCl(aq).   (3)
(c) 24.0 cm^3 of 0.5 mol l^{-1} sodium hydroxide solution neutralises 20.0 cm^3 of dilute *sulphuric acid*.   (3)
(Total: 9)

8. Refer back to unit 1 page 2, and use the data given in table 1 along with the equation for the reaction to calculate the concentration of hydrochloric acid at (i) 90 seconds, and (ii) 210 seconds.   [PS] (4)

SECTION B: Quantitative electrolysis (pages 53 to 54, worked example 3.1).

NB: Balanced ion-electron equations are an essential part of each calculation.

Total charge on 1 mole of electrons is 96500 C, (i.e. coulombs)

Quantity of electricity (C)
   = Current (A) × Time (s)

---

1. Calculate the mass of silver deposited on passing a current of 2 A through silver(I) nitrate solution for 30 minutes.   (3)

2. An electric current of 10 A is passed through molten magnesium chloride for 15 minutes. Calculate the mass of magnesium produced at the negative electrode.   (3)

3. During electrolysis of a dilute acid 0.25 g of hydrogen gas is collected. What mass of copper would be obtained if the same current is used for the same time in electrolysis of copper(II) chloride solution?   [PS](4)

4. When constant current was passed through chromium (III) sulphate solution for 48 minutes 15 seconds, 1.04 g of chromium was deposited. Calculate the current used.   (3)

5. A copper compound was known to contain either copper(I) or copper(II) ions. The compound was dissolved in water and electrolysed. It was found that 0.32 g of copper was formed after the electrolysis cell had been operating for 16 minutes with a steady current of 1.0 A.
(a) At which electrode would copper have been formed?   (1)
(b) Using the above information, determine which copper ion was present. Working must be shown.   [PS](3)
(SEB)(Total: 4)

6. Aluminium is obtained by molten electrolysis of aluminium oxide. This process is carried out in the Highland Region at Fort William and Kinlochleven. The Lochaber smelter at Fort William has 80 electrolytic cells connected in series operating at 175000 A. Each cell produces about 1300 kg of aluminium per day. The Kinlochleven smelter, which began production in 1907, has a total of 112 cells operating at 40000 A.
(a) Calculate the theoretical daily output of aluminium at each smelter (i) for each cell, and (ii) in total, assuming all the cells at Fort William are in operation and 100 cells at Kinlochleven.   (5)

(b) The smelters are operated by the same company. Use your answer to (a)(ii) to find what percentage of the combined daily output is produced at Fort William.   (1)

(c) In the electrolytic cell, the positive electrode consists of carbon which is literally burned away through combining with oxygen released at this electrode. Assuming complete combination of oxygen with carbon, calculate the mass of carbon needed per day in an electrolytic cell at Kinlochleven, using the equations :
$2O^{2-} \rightarrow O_2 + 4e^-$, and $C + O_2 \rightarrow CO_2$ (3)

(d) What do you think would be the main advantages and disadvantages of siting aluminium smelters in the Highland Region? (2)
[PS](Total: 11)

SECTION C: Avogadro Constant, L
(pages 54 to 55 and including worked examples 3.2 and 3.3).

$$L = 6.02 \times 10^{23}\,\text{mol}^{-1}$$

1. Calculate the number of atoms in
(a) 12 g of helium   (2)
(b) 12 g of magnesium   (2)
(c) a 2 kg gold bar.   (2)
(Total: 6)

2. A cube of aluminium has a side of length 10 cm. If each cm^3 of aluminium has a mass of 2.7 g, calculate the number of atoms of aluminium in the cube.   (SEB)[PS](4)

3. Calculate (i) the number of molecules, and (ii) the number of atoms in
(a) 16 g of oxygen   (3)
(b) 180 g of water   (3)
(c) 15.4 g of tetrachloromethane, CCl_4 (3)
(d) 3.42 g of sucrose, $C_{12}H_{22}O_{11}$: a spoonful of sugar!   (3)
(Total: 12)

4. When potassium chlorate ($KClO_3$) is heated strongly, it decomposes to give potassium chloride and oxygen.

Calculate the mass of potassium chlorate which would produce 1.8×10^{23} molecules of oxygen.   (SEB)[PS](3)

5. Calculate (i) the number of positive ions, and (ii) the number of negative ions in
(a) 450 g of sodium iodide, NaI   (3)
(b) 17.4 g of potassium sulphate, K_2SO_4 (3)
(c) 47 g of copper(II) nitrate, $Cu(NO_3)_2$ (3)
(d) 100 g of iron(III) sulphate, $Fe_2(SO_4)_3$ (3)
(Total: 12)

6. Calculate the number of moles of aluminium oxide that contains 3×10^{23} ions.
(SEB) [PS](3)

7. Calculate the mass of calcium phosphate which contains 3.6×10^{22} phosphate ions.   (SEB)[PS](3)

8. Calculate the number of
(a) calcium ions in a mixture of calcium chloride and calcium sulphate which contains 1 mole of chloride ions and 1.5 moles of sulphate ions   (2)
(b) chloride ions in a mixture of ammonium chloride and aluminium chloride which contains 0.1 moles of ammonium ions and 0.1 moles of aluminium ions.   (2)
[PS](Total: 4)

9. Calculate the number of electrons contained in 2.8 g of nitrogen gas.   (SEB)[PS](4)

10. Calculate the number of electrons in 9 g of aluminium ions, Al^{3+}.   [PS](3)

SECTION D: Gas Volumes
(pages 56 to 59, including worked examples 3.4, 3.5, 3.6 and 3.7).

1. Calculate the density in g l^{-1} of the following gases at room temperature and pressure. The molar volume under these conditions is 24 mol l^{-1}.
(a) Neon   (b) Ammonia   (c) Propane   (6)

2. A plastic bag had a capacity of 3.5 litres. Together with an inlet tube and stopper, the empty bag weighed 21.5 g. It was filled with a number of gases and reweighed under the same conditions of temperature and pressure. Allowing for buoyancy, two of the corrected weights are shown below.

Bag + Nitrogen   25.9 g

Bag + Carbon dioxide   28.4 g

(a) Use these figures to calculate the volume occupied by 1 mole of each of these gases under experimental conditions.   (3)
(b) What volume would you expect 1 mole of methane to occupy under the same conditions of temperature and pressure?   (1)
(SEB)(Total: 4)

3. Nitrogen monoxide gas, NO, combines with oxygen to form brown fumes of nitrogen dioxide according to the equation

$$2NO(g) + O_2(g) \rightarrow 2NO_2(g)$$

Calculate the volume of oxygen needed to react completely with 60 cm^3 of nitrogen monoxide, and the volume of nitrogen dioxide produced.   (2)

4. When 100 cm^3 of a gaseous hydrocarbon are burned in excess oxygen, 400 cm^3 of carbon dioxide and 400 cm^3 of water vapour are produced. (All measurements are at a temperature above 100°C and at 1 atmosphere pressure.)

(a) What is the molecular formula of the hydrocarbon?   (3)
(b) The hydrocarbon does not decolorise bromine water. Draw a possible structural formula for the hydrocarbon.
(SEB)[PS](Total: 4)

5. When subjected to a continuous electric spark, ammonia gas decomposes to form a gaseous mixture of nitrogen and hydrogen.
(a) Write a balanced equation for this reaction.   (1)
(b) Calculate the volume of each gas formed when 50 cm^3 of ammonia are completely decomposed.   (2)
(c) Predict the effect on the final volume if the products are tested with a burning splint.   [PS](1)
(Total: 4)

(NB: A balanced equation is an essential first step in questions 6 and 7.)

6. For each of the following gases, calculate (i) the volume of oxygen required for complete combustion, and (ii) the volume of carbon dioxide produced. All volumes are measured at the same conditions of room temperature and pressure.
(a) 200 cm^3 of methane
(b) 1 litre of butane
(c) 10 cm^3 of cyclopropane.   (9)

7. Given that the molar volume of a gas at room temperature and pressure is 24 l mol^{-1}, calculate the volume of gas produced when the following reactions go to completion.
(a) 21 g of magnesium carbonate are decomposed by heat   (3)
(b) 13 g of zinc are added to excess dilute hydrochloric acid   (3)
(c) Excess zinc is added to 100 cm^3 of 2 mol l^{-1} hydrochloric acid.   (2)
(In examples (b) and (c) the salt formed is zinc(II) chloride).   (Total: 8)

SECTION E: Identify a reactant in excess (pages 59 to 60, including worked examples 3.8 and 3.9).

(NB: Balanced equations are required in questions 1 to 4.)

1. Show by calculation which reactant in the following examples is present in excess. Also, calculate the volume and composition of the resulting gas mixture, assuming that all volumes are measured at the same room temperature and pressure.
   (a) A mixture of $10 \, cm^3$ methane and $25 \, cm^3$ oxygen was burned. (3)
   (b) A mixture of $10 \, cm^3$ propane and $25 \, cm^3$ oxygen was burned. (3)
   (Total: 6)

2. (a) Write a balanced equation for the complete combustion of ethyne (C_2H_2). (1)
   (b) If $50 \, cm^3$ of ethyne are burned completely in $220 \, cm^3$ of oxygen, what will be the volume and composition of the resulting gas mixture? (All volumes are measured under the same conditions of temperature and pressure.) (3)
   (SEB)(Total: 4)

3. For each of the following examples of neutralisation: (i) show by calculation which reactant is present in excess, and (ii) calculate the mass of salt which would be produced.
   (a) 8 g copper(II) oxide were added to $50 \, cm^3$ of 1 mol l^{-1} H_2SO_4(aq). (4)
   (b) 2.67 g of lead(II) carbonate were added to $60 \, cm^3$ of 0.5 mol l^{-1} HNO_3(aq). (4)
   (c) 8.1 g of aluminium were added to $150 \, cm^3$ of 2 mol l^{-1} hydrochloric acid. (4)
   (Total: 12)

4. $10 \, cm^3$ of 2 mol l^{-1} sodium sulphate solution is added to $25 \, cm^3$ of 1 mol l^{-1} barium chloride solution. Show by calculation which reactant is in excess and calculate the mass of precipitate formed. [PS](4)

5. A mixture of $80 \, cm^3$ CO and $150 \, cm^3$ O_2 was exploded.
   (a) Write a balanced equation for the reaction. (1)

   After cooling the residual gas was shaken with sodium hydroxide solution.
   (b) Which gas would be absorbed by the sodium hydroxide? (1)
   (c) What would be the reduction in volume of residual gas on shaking with the sodium hydroxide? (1)
   (d) What volume of gas would remain? (1)
   (Assume all volumes are measured at s.t.p.) (SEB)(Total: 4)

SECTION F: Percentage yield
(page 61, including worked example 3.10).

$$\text{Percentage yield} = \frac{\text{actual yield}}{\text{theoretical yield}} \times 100\%$$

(NB: Balanced equations are required in questions 1 and 2.)

1. Calculate the percentage yield of product in each of the following examples.
   (a) 6.2 g of copper(II) carbonate when decomposed by heat gave 3.8 g of copper(II) oxide. (3)
   (b) 0.8 g of calcium when dissolved in excess dilute hydrochloric acid gave $432 \, cm^3$ of hydrogen gas at room temperature and pressure. The molar volume under these conditions is 24 mol l^{-1}. (3)
   (Total: 6)

2. 2.0 g of copper(II) oxide was dissolved in excess dilute sulphuric acid. Calculate the mass of hydrated copper(II) sulphate crystals, $CuSO_4.5H_2O$, obtained if the percentage yield is 80%. (3)

3. In theory, one mole of benzene, C_6H_6, can be converted to one mole of methylbenzene, $C_6H_5CH_3$, which in turn can yield one mole of benzoic acid, C_6H_5COOH. In an experiment, 0.1 mole of benzene produced 4.6 g of methylbenzene which was then converted to benzoic acid, the percentage yield for this reaction being 70%. Calculate:

    (i) the percentage yield for the first reaction (2)

    (ii) the mass of benzoic acid finally obtained, (2)

    (iii) the overall percentage yield of benzoic acid based on the original quantity of benzene. [PS](1)

                    (Total: 5)

SECTION G: Redox reactions

(pages 62 to 69, including worked examples 3.11 and 3.12).

1. In each of the examples in the table below use the ion-electron equations given to

    (i) decide which reactant is the reducing agent and which the oxidising agent, and

    (ii) write the balanced redox equation for the overall reaction.

2. In each of the following examples write the ion-electron equation and indicate whether the change is a reduction or an oxidation.

    (a) Manganese(IV) oxide, $MnO_2(s)$, in the presence of water
        $\rightarrow$ Permanganate ions, $MnO_4^-(aq)$ (2)

    (b) Nitrate ions in acid solution
        $\rightarrow$ Ammonium ions (2)

    (c) Ferrate ions, $FeO_4^{2-}(aq)$, in acid solution $\rightarrow$ Iron(II) ions, $Fe^{3+}(aq)$ (2)

    (d) Vanadium(II) ions, $V^{2+}(aq)$
        $\rightarrow$ Vanadate ions, $VO_3^-(aq)$ (2)
                    (Total: 8)

3. (a) In acid solution, iodate ions, $IO_3^-(aq)$, are readily converted into iodine. Write an ion-electron equation for this half-reaction. (2)
    (b) Use the equation to explain whether the iodate ion is an oxidising or reducing agent. (2)
               (SEB)(Total: 4)

Reactants	Ion-electron equations	
(a) Iodine solution and Sulphite solution	$I_2 + 2e^- \rightarrow 2I^-$ $SO_3^{2-} + H_2O \rightarrow SO_4^{2-} + 2H^+ + 2e^-$	(2)
(b) Iron(II) solution and Hydrogen peroxide solution	$Fe^{2+} \rightarrow Fe^{3+} + e^-$ $H_2O_2 + 2H^+ + 2e^- \rightarrow 2H_2O$	(2)
(c) Tin(II) solution and Dichromate solution	$Sn^{2+} \rightarrow Sn^{4+} + 2e^-$ $Cr_2O_7^{2-} + 14H^+ + 6e^- \rightarrow 2Cr^{3+} + 7H_2O$	(2)
(d) Permanganate solution and Hydrogen peroxide solution	$MnO_4^- + 8H^+ + 5e^- \rightarrow Mn^{2+} + 4H_2O$ $H_2O_2 \rightarrow O_2 + 2H^+ + 2e^-$	(2)

                    (Total: 8)

4. Use the balanced redox equations derived in question **1** on page 75 to calculate the concentration of the solution in italics.

(a) 12.5 cm^3 of an *iodine solution* reacts with 20.0 cm^3 of 0.1 mol l^{-1} sulphite solution. (2)

(b) 25.0 cm^3 of an *iron (II) solution* reacts with 20.0 cm^3 of 0.5 mol l^{-1} hydrogen peroxide solution. (2)

(c) 15.0 cm^3 of *tin (II) solution* reacts with 25.0 cm^3 of 0.2 mol l^{-1} dichromate solution. (2)

(d) 10.0 cm^3 of *hydrogen peroxide solution* reacts with 20.0 cm^3 of 0.02 mol l^{-1} permanganate solution. (2)

(Total: 8)

4 Biomolecules

From previous work you should *know* and *understand*:

a) The meaning of unsaturation in carbon compounds.
b) The result of the addition of hydrogen to alkenes.
c) The meaning of condensation polymerisation. (See also unit 2 pages 24/26.)
d) Carbohydrates as a source of energy for the body.
e) Condensation and hydrolysis of carbohydrates. The function of enzymes.
f) Alcohols (unit 2 pages 31/35.)
g) Carboxylic acids (unit 2 pages 20 and 37/38.)

FATS AND OILS

Fats and oils can be of animal, vegetable or marine origin. Some animal and vegetable oils and fats are listed below.

Vegetable	*Animal*
Soyabean oil	Whale oil
Palm oil	Cod liver oil
Olive oil	Pork fat: lard
Castor oil	Mutton fat ⎤ tallow
Linseed oil	Beef fat ⎦

Vegetable oils are usually pressed out of the seed of the appropriate plant – rape seed oil is the only oil produced in the UK. Whale oil is now only produced by three countries since international agreements to protect the whale were introduced. Animal fats are extracted by 'rendering down' fatty parts of the appropriate animal. Suet is such a material.

Oils and fats differ physically only in that oils are above their melting points and hence are liquid whereas fats are, of course, solid. Under cold conditions some vegetable oils may become cloudy, or even solidify.

The low melting points of oils are caused by more of their molecules being unsaturated, i.e. containing carbon to carbon double bonds. Their 'degree of unsaturation' is higher than that of fats.

Shaking of oils with bromine water results in the bromine water being readily decolourised. The decolourisation is the standard test for unsaturation. If solutions of fats in a saturated organic solvent are treated in this way, decolourisation is not so rapid. The test can be modified to estimate quantitatively the degree of unsaturation of various oils and fats.

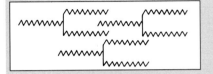

Figure 1 Diagrammatic representation of the structure of fat molecules

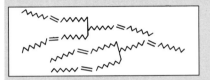

Figure 2 An exaggerated picture of oil molecules

Fat and oil molecules are roughly 'tuning-fork' shaped, with the three limbs consisting of hydrocarbon chains (figures 1 and 2). If the chains are saturated, the molecules can pack neatly together, even at quite high temperatures.

If the chains contain one or more double bonds, the zig-zag chains become more distorted and close packing of molecules is less easy unless even more thermal energy is removed (i.e. the oils have lower melting points).

Since oils differ chemically from fats by being unsaturated, hardening of oils can be carried out by addition of hydrogen across the double bonds.

Ethene can be converted to ethane by addition of hydrogen:

$$
\underset{\text{H}}{\overset{\text{H}}{\text{C}}}\!=\!\underset{\text{H}}{\overset{\text{H}}{\text{C}}} \quad + \quad \text{H}-\text{H} \quad \xrightarrow[\text{catalyst}]{\text{Ni}} \quad \text{H}-\underset{\text{H}}{\overset{\text{H}}{\text{C}}}-\underset{\text{H}}{\overset{\text{H}}{\text{C}}}-\text{H}
$$

Similarly oils can be converted to fats by the use of hydrogen with nickel catalysts:

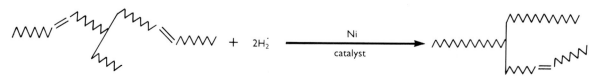

Figure 3 Partial hydrogenation of an oil molecule

The degree of unsaturation is now less than that of the original oil.

Margarine is made by hydrogenation, i.e. partially hardening vegetable oils using hydrogen and a nickel catalyst in the warm oil. The catalyst is then removed from the product which hardens on cooling.

There is some evidence to suggest that saturated fats are more liable to cause heart disease than unsaturated fats. The evidence is not clear-cut and recently suggestions have emerged that fish oils may be especially beneficial in reducing heart disease. General opinion seems to be that too much fat is to be avoided and it is wiser to err on the side of unsaturated rather than saturated fat. Fats and oils provide a source of fat soluble vitamins A and D. These are naturally present in dairy products, and are now a legally required additive in margarines to prevent vitamin deficiency problems such as 'rickets'.

The major dietary function of fats and oils is to provide energy in the body. They provide more energy than carbohydrates, but it is released much more slowly (table 1).

Foodstuff	Energy yield kJ/100 g
Sucrose (sugar)	1672
Sunflower oil	3700
Cooking margarine	3006
'Low fat' spread	1569
Butter	3140
White bread	961

Table 1

In terms of controlling 'calories' it is obviously beneficial to cut down on fatty food rather than on carbohydrates.

A major use of oils is in paints. Their unsaturated nature allows them to harden by the uptake of oxygen. Linseed oil, from flax, is especially important in this context.

At present 'linoleum' is making a comeback as a floor covering. Unlike the new PVC floor covering it is claimed to be environmentally friendly. Linoleum also uses linseed oil as a raw material (figure 4).

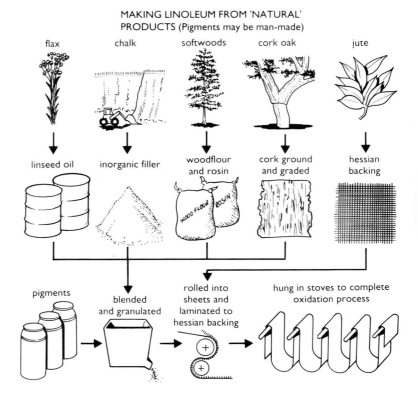

MAKING LINOLEUM FROM 'NATURAL' PRODUCTS (Pigments may be man-made)

Figure 4

Various vegetable oils are now being used in the production of bio-degradable detergents. A simple detergent can be made by treating castor oil with concentrated sulphuric acid and then neutralising the product with sodium hydroxide solution.

HYDROLYSIS OF FATS AND OILS

When fats or oils are treated with superheated steam they break up, *hydrolyse*, into a substance known as glycerol (left) and various 'fatty acids'.

Glycerol is an alcohol with three –OH groups per molecule – a *trihydric* alcohol.

The 'fatty acids' are straight chain carboxylic acids (see unit 2 pages 20 and 37/38) which may be saturated (alkanoic acids) or unsaturated (alkenoic acids) which contain even numbers of carbon atoms ranging from C_4 to C_{24} but primarily C_{16} and C_{18}. Some contain –OH substituent groups.

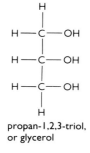

propan-1,2,3-triol, or glycerol

e.g.

Palmitic acid $CH_3(CH_2)_{14}COOH$
Stearic acid $CH_3(CH_2)_{16}COOH$
Oleic acid $CH_3(CH_2)_7CH = CH(CH_2)_7COOH$
Linoleic acid $CH_3(CH_2)_3(CH_2CH=CH_2)_2(CH_2)_7COOH$
Ricinoleic acid $CH_3(CH_2)_5CH(OH)CH_2CH=CH(CH_2)_7COOH$

These names are of course trivial names. Stearic acid is octadecanoic acid according to IUPAC usage. Fats and oils contain glycerol combined with fatty acids in the ratio of one mole of glycerol to three moles of fatty acid.

No fat or oil is a pure 'triglyceride' as these compounds are called, but a mixture of many. Indeed in any triglyceride the three acid molecules combined with one molecule of glycerol may or may not be identical, e.g. one triglyceride is:

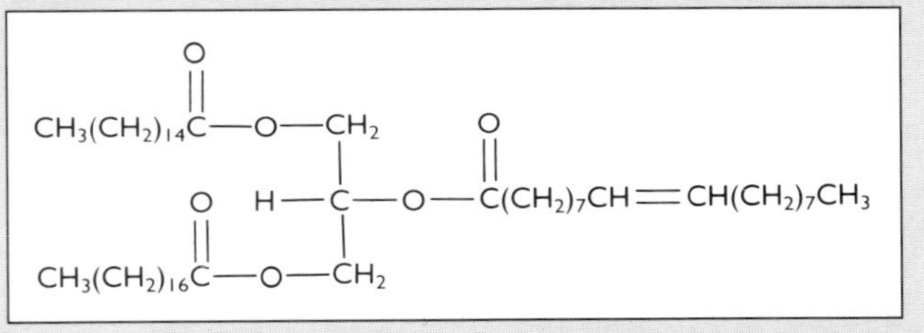

This is called 'Palmito – oleo – stearin' and the number of possible triglycerides is very large.

This structure appears very complicated, but in fact is evidence that fats and oils are very complex examples of a class of organic compounds called *esters* dealt with in unit 4 pages 83/85.

SOAPS

It is important to realise that soaps, which appear briefly in Standard Grade, are made by the alkaline hydrolysis of fats and oils by sodium or potassium hydroxide. The glycerol liberated is an important raw material and the fatty acids are produced in the form of their sodium or potassium salts. These salts are 'soap'. Since they are soluble they must be extracted from the hydrolysis mixture by adding a large excess of sodium chloride, after which the soap can be filtered off. *Palmolive* obviously takes its name from palm oil and olive oil. *SR toothpaste* was apparently named from sodium ricinoleate, a soap, made from castor oil, which was described as an ingredient in early TV advertising.

Soaps are useful for cleaning because of the structure of the ion liberated when they dissolve in water (figure 5):

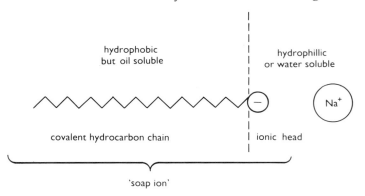

Figure 5 The structure of a 'soap ion'

The covalent 'tail' bonds to the similar greasy material on fabric or skin, the ionic head is attracted to the polar covalent water molecules. An emulsion of globules of grease in water is formed as shown in figure 6.

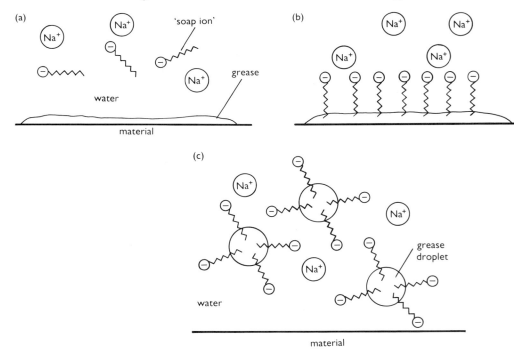

Figure 6 Greasy material being washed by soapy water

ESTERS

Compounds formed by condensation from an alkanol and an alkanoic acid are esters:

e.g.

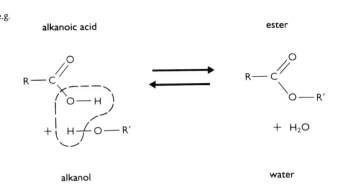

R and R′ represent variable alkyl groups.

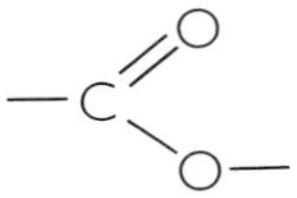

is the ester linkage

e.g. CH_3-C is ethyl ethanoate
$O-C_2H_5$

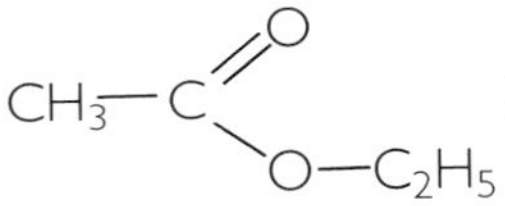

formed from: CH_3-C and C_2H_5OH
$O-H$

ethanoic acid   ethanol

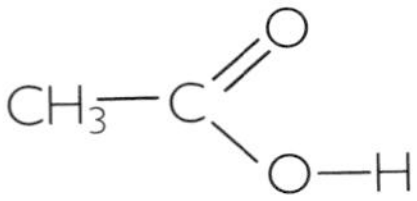

and

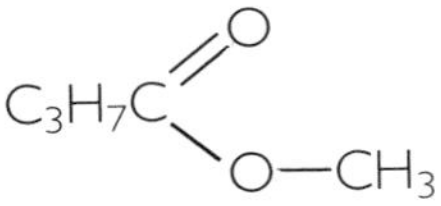

C_3H_7C is methyl butanoate
$O-CH_3$

formed from: C_3H_7C and CH_3OH
$O-H$

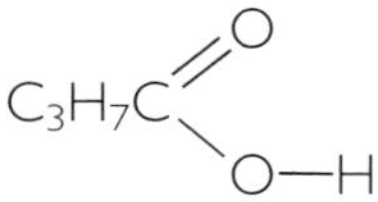

butanoic acid   methanol

(Note the usual convention for drawing the structural formula and writing the name. In the formula the alkanol component is second, but in the name it is first.)

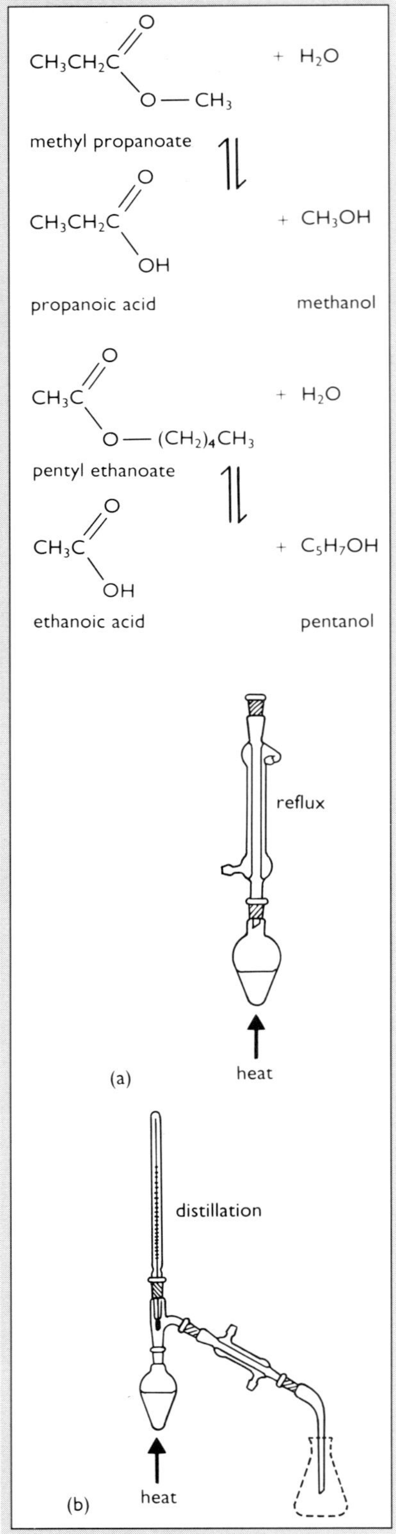

The triglyceride shown in the previous section can be seen to contain three ester linkages. The general equation for the formation of esters contained the sign $\rightleftharpoons$ indicating that the reaction is reversible. Heating an ester with water or steam will therefore, as for oils and fats, result in hydrolysis, i.e. the ester splits up to form its parent alkanol and alkanoic acid. 2 examples are shown on the left.

The reversibility of the reaction means that to form an ester, it is necessary to warm the parent alkanol and acid together on a water bath, in the presence of a little concentrated sulphuric acid to absorb the water produced and increase the yield of ester. The ester can be isolated by fractional distillation; or merely detected by smell by pouring onto cold water. The ester, being oily, forms a layer on the water whilst the other substances present dissolve in the water.

The reversibility also means that hydrolysis can be incomplete. To hydrolyse esters completely it is usual to use alkali solution and reflux the mixture for a long time (figure 7(a))

The alkanol is liberated, along with the sodium salt of the alkanoic acid. The alkanol can be distilled off after the apparatus is reassembled appropriately (figure 7(b)), and then the solution is acidified with HCl when the alkanoic acid is formed.

Esters are very versatile compounds. Most of them are pleasant smelling liquids, having boiling points dependent on their molecular masses. Being covalently bonded, but with a polar covalent $\diagup C = O$, they will dissolve in covalent and some polar covalent substances but are not very miscible with water. Some of the more volatile esters are used as solvents where rapid evaporation is required e.g. ethyl ethanoate is used in adhesives and pentyl ethanoate isomers are used in nail varnish. Other esters are used as flavourings and in perfumes as in table 2. It is worth noting that natural flavourings are more subtle blends of esters, although containing those mentioned in the table.

Figure 7

Name	Structural formula	Odour/flavour
pentyl ethanoate	$CH_3COO(CH_2)_4CH_3$	banana
octyl ethanoate	$CH_3COO(CH_2)_7CH_3$	orange
methyl butanoate	$CH_3(CH_2)_2COOCH_3$	pineapple
pentyl butanoate	$CH_3(CH_2)_2COO(CH_2)_4CH_3$	apricot
3methylbutyl butanoate	$CH_3(CH_2)_2COO(CH_2)_2CH(CH_3)_2$	pear
3methylbutyl3methylbutanoate	$(CH_3)_2CHCH_2COO(CH_2)_2CH(CH_3)_2$	apple

Table 2

As mentioned in unit 2 page 22, diacids and diols can link alternatively to produce polyesters used as fibre. More complex substances produce resins. If a chain type polyester is produced, it is suitable for use as fibre. Cross linked polyester resins with a three dimensional structure are suitable for moulding. In the former the chain is strong but flexible, in the latter the network is strong but rigid. One trademark for polyester fibre is 'Terylene' which is formed from *tere*phthalic acid and eth*ylene* glycol. The rigid polymer is used to make soft drink bottles, which can be recycled.

PROTEINS

Proteins make up a huge variety of animal and plant material of which the following are examples:

(i) peas and beans
(ii) meat
(iii) fish
(iv) cheese
(v) eggs
(vi) hides and skin
(vii) wool and silk

Although proteins can be grouped into categories, such as the above, there can be large structural variations within each division. For example, category (ii) would contain such proteins as beef, chicken, mutton and pork which are all different from each other. Variation also occurs within the individual animal itself, for example muscle, kidney and liver proteins.

All proteins on heating with soda lime (a mixture of sodium and calcium hydroxides which is very strongly alkaline) yield acrid smelling alkaline gases (figure 8). Such gases are all amines or ammonia, i.e. nitrogen- containing substances. Hence all proteins contain nitrogen and we can begin to understand why plants require soluble nitrogen compounds as an essential nutrient. Without it plants cannot synthesise protein. Animals cannot synthesise protein from simple nitrogen compounds but they can reconstruct vegetable or other animal protein. All protein is derived therefore from the fixation of atmospheric nitrogen as nitrates in soil.

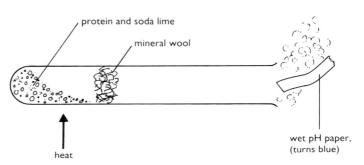

Figure 8 Protein mixed with soda lime and then heated

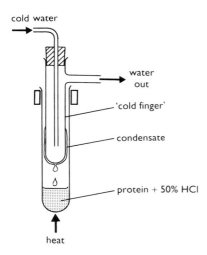

Figure 9 Protein being hydrolysed with 50% hydrochloric acid

If protein is hydrolysed using 50% hydrochloric acid, refluxing the mixture for several hours, then the protein breaks down into its constituents called *amino acids*. Figure 4.9 illustrates suitable apparatus for a small scale experiment. Alternatively the reflux apparatus of figure 7(a) can be used.

These amino acids have a typical structure:

R again represents a variable organic group (or hydrogen).

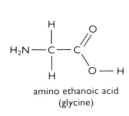

amino ethanoic acid
(glycine)

2–amino propanoic acid
(alanine)

The simplest amino acids are glycine and alanine (left).

Twenty amino acids occur frequently in proteins, another six occur occasionally. The amino acids produced by hydrolysis of proteins can be identified, with difficulty, by chromatography as in figure 10.

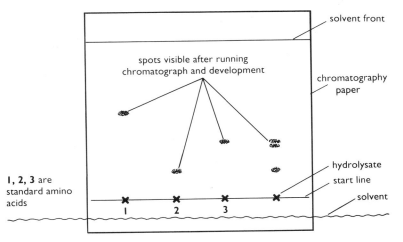

Figure 10 Chromatography of a protein hydrolysate and standard amino acids

The diagram shows the results of simple ascending chromatography. The protein hydrolysate is spotted onto filter paper, with solutions of known amino acids alongside. The paper is placed in a tank containing a solvent of propanol and water. When the solvent front has almost reached the top of the paper, the paper is removed and then the colourless amino acids are made visible by spraying with ninhydrin. The paper is then heated after which pink, blue or brown spots appear on the paper. In the example shown, the protein hydrolysate appears to contain amino acids '2' and '3' and some other amino acid which is not '1'.

In practice the separation achieved by this method is not good so two-way chromatography is used with two different solvents. Figure 11 illustrates the result of such an experiment.

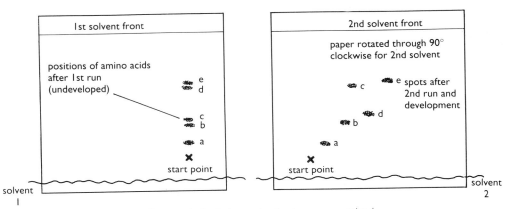

Figure 11 Chromatography of a protein hydrolysate by the two-way method

The same protein hydrolysate is used on its own and the paper placed for a fixed time in each solvent in turn. After removal from the second solvent, development with ninhydrin is carried out. To identify the resultant spots, the same process is repeated under identical conditions with each amino acid in turn on separate sheets of paper. The spots are identified by superimposing these separate chromatograms on the original hydrolysate chromatogram.

THE FORMATION AND BREAKDOWN OF PROTEINS

The amino acids in a protein are linked similarly to polyamides (indicated in unit 2, page 21) in chains.

e.g.

The groups on the left are called amide or peptide links and when hydrolysis occurs these links break with the addition of an H— and an —OH at these positions. The three amino acids formed from the above protein fragment are

peptide links

Conversely when amino acids come together to form protein they do so by loss of water – *condensation polymerisation*.

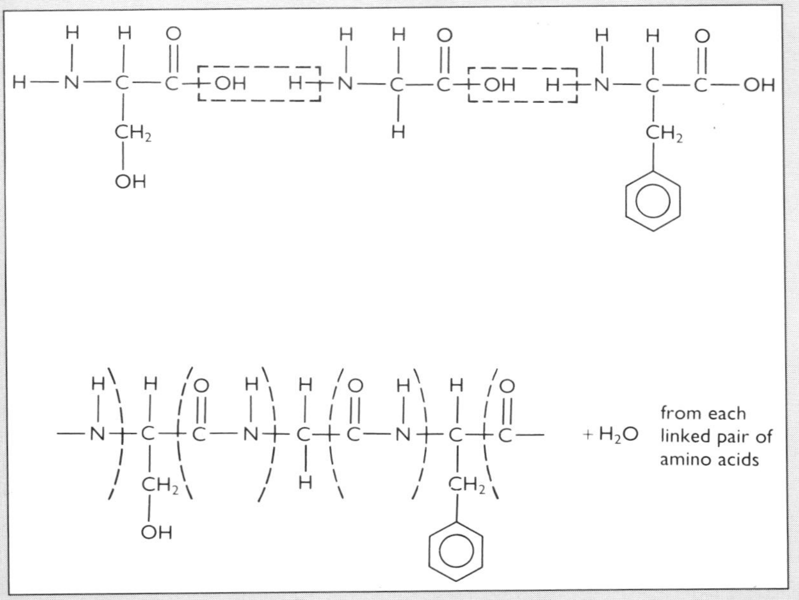

The protein chains can contain several thousand amino acids and hence protein molecules have huge molecular masses. The variety of proteins is caused by the possibility of arranging up to 26 amino acids in varying numbers and in varying orders into these long chains. In effect an alphabet of amino acids is assembled into a dictionary – full of proteins.

Proteins comprise a large part of an animal's diet. During digestion the animal and vegetable proteins in foodstuffs are hydrolysed into their component amino acids which are small enough molecules to pass into the bloodstream. Proteins required for the body's specific needs are built up from amino acids in the body cells according to information supplied by DNA in the cell nuclei.

Some of the amino acids required can be synthesised in the body, but others, called essential amino acids have to be present in dietary protein which is one important reason for consuming a wide enough variety of foodstuffs.

A fairly recent development is the commercial production of a derivative of a compound of aspartic acid and phenylalanine which is marketed as a sweetener under tradenames such as *Nutrasweet* or *Candarel*. Since it is hydrolysed to simple amino acids in the stomach it should be completely free of hazard. There is a difficulty, however, for people who have a congenital problem with phenylalanine in their diet. Such people are normally aware of the problem and can avoid these sweeteners.

ENZYMES

Enzymes are organic catalysts and all contain protein. Some are wholly protein, some require another organic or inorganic group – a co-enzyme – to activate them.

Each enzyme catalyses a specific reaction which is well demonstrated in a fermentation sequence from starch to ethanol:

$$\text{amylose (starch)} \xrightarrow{\text{amylase}} \text{maltose} \xrightarrow{\text{maltase}} \text{glucose} \xrightarrow{\text{'zymase'}} \text{ethanol} + CO_2$$

'Zymase' is actually a complex mixture of enzymes each of which assists a step in the reaction sequence from glucose to ethanol. See also unit 1 page 12.

Generally enzyme names end in '–ase'. They are often grouped as 'lipases' – fat digesting enzymes and 'proteinases' – protein digesting enzymes etc.

It is believed that enzymes work by the 'lock and key' principle. The complex shape of the protein which is the enzyme only allows certain 'substrate' molecules to fit into it. Only these molecules have their reactions influenced by the enzyme (see figure 12).

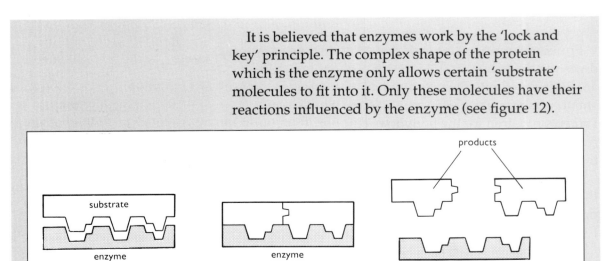

Figure 12 The 'lock and key' principle. A complex molecule being split by an enzyme

One enzyme is lysozyme which is a globular protein with a long narrow cleft in its side. A long cellulose type substrate molecule fits into this cleft. Whilst there, the chain of the substrate is broken and the parts are then released. Lysozyme is present in tears and other body secretions and is capable of breaking down the material of bacterial cell walls.

It is noteworthy that the activity of enzymes is lost at a little above 40°C and at low pH. This is not surprising since all proteins are *denatured* (i.e. have their structures changed) if temperatures rise or if they are acidified. Cooking an egg, for example, is intended to denature protein with a view to making it more palatable. A fried egg is a denatured egg!

Examples for practice

1. Sucrose can be represented by the structural formula below.

(a) Draw a circle round a primary alcohol group. (1)

(b) A fatty acid molecule can be represented thus:

Molecules like this can form ester links with molecules like sucrose. Change the above structure to show *one* such ester link formed with *one* fatty acid molecule. (1)

(c) If you had continued to complete all the possible sites in sucrose with this ester linkage, you would have drawn the structural formula of 'sucrose polyester'. 'Sucrose polyester' is an ideal ingredient in food for slimmers, since it is not digested in our bodies.

Suggest why 'sucrose polyester' is *not* hydrolysed by the enzymes in our digestive systems. (1)

(d)

A

B

Molecules like A and B can be used to make a linear polyester.

(i) Explain why molecules like A and B *cannot* be used to make a polyester resin. (1)

(ii) Explain why sucrose polyester is neither a linear polyester *nor* a polyester resin. (SEB)(1)

(Total: 5)

2.

The structure of a dipeptide with groups labelled: $HO-\underset{\parallel}{\underset{O}{C}}-\underset{\underset{CH_2}{|}}{CH}-NH-\underset{\parallel}{\underset{O}{C}}-CH\underset{NH_2}{\overset{|}{}}-CH_2-\underset{\parallel}{\underset{O}{C}}-OH$ with a phenyl ring attached to CH_2.

This dipeptide forms the two amino acids – aspartic acid and phenylalanine – when it is hydrolysed.

(a) Identify the amide link in the above structure by placing brackets around it. (1)
(b) Identify the phenyl group in the above structure, by circling it. (1)
(c) Draw the structure of the amino acid phenylalanine. (1)
(d) The artificial sweetener, aspartame, is a methyl ester of the dipeptide shown above. Its sweetness depends on the shape and structure of the molecule.

Suggest a reason why aspartame is *not* used in food that will be cooked, but is used in cold drinks, for example. (SEB)[PS](2)
(Total: 5)

3. The formulae for certain compounds are shown below. All the questions, unless otherwise stated, are about the compounds shown. Give your answer as the letter, or letters, used in the grid. A letter may be used more than once in different answers.

$C_{13}H_{27}COOH$ CH_2OH $C_2H_5NH_2$
             |
             CH_2OH

A   **B**   **C**

CH_2OH (ring) **D** $CONHCH_3$ (ring) **E** $COOC_2H_5$ (ring) **F**

$H_2NCHCOOH$ (ring) **G** $COOH$ (ring) $COOH$ **H** $C_{11}H_{21}COOH$ **I**

(a) Which compounds are alcohols? (2)
(b) Which compound is an ester? (1)
(c) Which pair of compounds when reacted together can form a polyester? (1)
(d) Which single compound can polymerise by a condensation mechanism? (1)
(e) Which of the compounds is an alkanoic acid? (1)
(f) Which compound contains an amide link? (1)
(g) Give the formula of a compound, not in the grid, which could react with compound H to form a polyamide. (1)
(Total: 8)

4. The following is part of a protein chain (the bond angles are not correctly shown):

$$-N-\underset{H}{\overset{CH_3}{\overset{|}{CH}}}-\underset{\parallel}{\underset{O}{C}}-\underset{H}{\overset{|}{N}}-CH_2-\underset{\parallel}{\underset{O}{C}}-\underset{H}{\overset{|}{N}}-\underset{H}{\overset{CH_3}{\overset{|}{CH}}}-\underset{\parallel}{\underset{O}{C}}-\underset{H}{\overset{|}{N}}-CH_2-\underset{\parallel}{\underset{O}{C}}-$$

Draw a structure of two amino acids obtained on hydrolysis of this protein. (SEB)(2)

5. Casein (a protein); olive oil; polystyrene; starch.

(a) Which of the above compounds is
 (i) not a macromolecule,
 (ii) not a natural product? (2)
(b) Choose *two* of the following processes and describe briefly how they could be carried out in the laboratory.
 (i) Acid hydrolysis of casein
 (ii) Production of soap from olive oil
 (iii) Enzyme hydrolysis of starch. (4)
(c) (i) A section of casein is shown here.

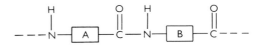

Draw the structural formulae of the two compounds formed when this section is hydrolysed. (2)

(d)

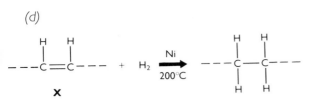

X

X represents part of the structure of olive oil.
  (i) Why is this reaction important and what is the function of 'Ni' in the reaction? (2)
  (ii) Use bond enthalpy data from your data book to calculate the enthalpy change of this reaction. (2)
                    (Total: 12)

6. $C_6H_{12}O_6 : C_2H_5OH : C_3H_6 : CH_3COOH : C_8H_{18}$
     P   Q   R   S   T

(a) Which of the above compounds at room temperature is
  (i) a gas,
  (ii) a solid? (1)

(b) Choose *two* of the following changes and describe briefly how they could be carried out in the laboratory.
  (i) P→Q (ii) Q→S (iii) T→R (4)
(c) The formula of R could represent two compounds with different structural formulae. One of these compounds is unsaturated while the other is saturated.
  (i) Draw the two possible structural formulae and give their chemical names. (3)
  (ii) Which of the two structures is likely to polymerise and by what type of reaction? Draw a structural formula to show the result of linking together three monomer molecules. (2)

(d) 0.01 mole of compound T was burnt and the heat released raised the temperature of 1 kg of water through 13.0°C. Use this data to calculate the heat of combustion of T. (2)
                    (Total: 12)

5 From bonds to behaviour

In this chapter, you will see that the properties of elements and compounds are related to the types of bonding present. You should know and understand the following Standard Grade topics.

a) Periodicity, Atom Structure
b) Covalent Bonding
c) Ionic Bonding
d) Physical Properties of Metals.

BONDING IN ELEMENTS

The 'Noble Gases'

The bonding in the elements is least complex at the right hand side of the Periodic Table i.e. for the 'Noble Gases'. These elements, with the exception of Helium, always have an outer layer of eight electrons which is an especially stable arrangement. Because of the stability of the outer electrons, the 'Noble Gases' do not form either covalent or ionic bonds between their atoms. They are 'monatomic' i.e. their molecules consist of only one atom.

Although there are no ionic or covalent bonds between the atoms, there are however other very weak forces. These forces are caused by the uneven distribution of the constantly moving electrons around the nuclei of the atoms. This causes temporary 'dipoles' on the atoms, see figure 1. The atoms then attract each other. The dipoles are constantly changing, but there are always some in existence.

These forces are called van der Waals' forces and are very weak compared with ionic and covalent bonds, being of the order of 1–10 kJmol^{-1} rather than 100–400 kJmol^{-1}. Although so weak, the van der Waals' forces are strong enough to allow the 'Noble Gases' to liquify and solidify if they are cooled enough to remove the thermal kinetic energy of the atoms. Not surprisingly, helium, with only two electrons per atom, has the weakest van der Waals'

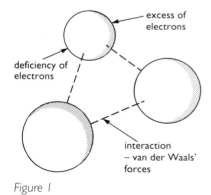

excess of electrons

deficiency of electrons

interaction – van der Waals' forces

Figure 1

forces between its atoms and is the most difficult element to condense and freeze. It only freezes in temperatures near to absolute zero.

Groups VII, VI and V

In Groups VII, VI and V, the structures of the elements are based on covalent bond formation to achieve eight outer electrons.

GROUP VII ELEMENTS
The halogens with one unpaired outer electron can form one covalent bond, and as a result diatomic molecules F_2, Cl_2, Br_2 and I_2 are formed. These molecules interact only weakly by the van der Waals' mechanism so that all the elements are volatile, and fluorine and chlorine are gaseous.

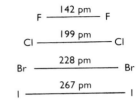

Figure 2 Bonding in the halogen molecules

GROUP VI ELEMENTS
Oxygen Each oxygen atom uses its two unpaired electrons to form two covalent bonds with one other oxygen atom (except when the rarer form ozone, O_3, is formed). The molecules interact by van der Waals' bonding but since the interaction is weak, O_2 is gaseous.

Sulphur When they have the ability to form two or more bonds, atoms can bond to more than one other atom. In the case of sulphur, closed eight membered puckered rings are found in the crystalline forms, and zig-zag chains are found in plastic sulphur.

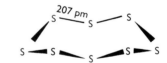

Figure 3 Bonding in oxygen and sulphur

GROUP V ELEMENTS
Nitrogen Nitrogen atoms form diatomic molecules with a triple bond, and only weak van der Waals' interaction.

Phosphorus Phosphorus makes use of single bonds to three other atoms to form tetrahedral P_4 molecules.

   In the elements of groups VII, VI and V, the *intramolecular* forces, i.e. the bonds *within* the molecule are covalent. The *intermolecular* forces, those *between* the molecules are the very weak van der Waals' forces. Most of these elements are therefore quite volatile, even if solid at room temperature, since only the intermolecular forces have to be broken to melt and boil them.

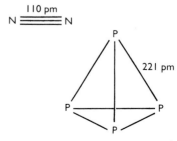

Figure 4 Bonding in nitrogen and phosphorus

Group IV Elements

The standard structure of the group is an infinite three dimensional network or lattice as in diamond and silicon. Each atom bonds covalently to four other atoms. The resultant structure is exceptionally hard and rigid. There are no discrete molecules, each atom being linked to each other atom in the piece of the element. There are no free electrons to allow conduction but in diamonds, for example, 'tunnels' between the atoms allow light to pass through, thus making them transparent.

Graphite, the other variety of carbon, shown in figure 6, has a structure based on three covalent bonds from each atom in one plane, forming layers of hexagonal rings. Each carbon atom contributes its fourth unpaired electron to delocalised orbitals extending over the layers. The result is strong bonding within the layers but only weak interaction between the layers. Since the delocalised electrons are held quite weakly, they can flow across the layers.

Graphite therefore conducts, similarly to a metal. The layers separate easily so graphite is flaky, but because the layers are offset with respect to each other, light cannot pass through, so graphite is opaque.

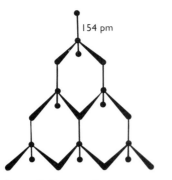

Figure 5 Diamond

154 pm

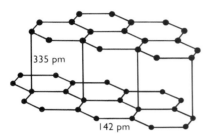

335 pm

142 pm

Figure 6 Graphite

Groups I, II and III

Elements in these groups have insufficient electrons to allow the achievement of an octet of electrons in their outer layer by covalent bonding. Generally the elements contribute their outer electrons to a common 'pool' of delocalised electrons, which act as a binding medium for the resultant positive ions. The bonding is less directional than covalent bonding, and the metals are therefore malleable* and ductile*. The electrons are capable of easy movements and hence the elements are electrical conductors. They are typical metals, and the above describes *metallic bonding*.

The one exception of any note in Groups I, II and III is boron. This forms a structure made up of B_{12} groups, which are interbonded with other groups. The result is an element almost as hard as diamond. The explanation of the bonding in boron is complex, as is that of the bonding of boron compounds.

* malleable – can be beaten
  or rolled into sheets
* ductile – can be drawn
  into wire

Summary of structures of first 20 elements

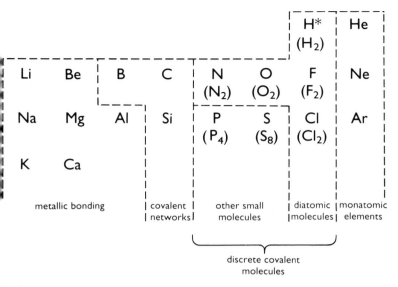

*Hydrogen is *not* a member of Group VII

Figure 7 Summary of the structure of elements 1 to 20

PHYSICAL PROPERTIES OF ELEMENTS RELATED TO BONDING

If we now look at some histograms of the physical properties of these first 20 elements, we can see how these properties relate to the bond types present.

Melting and boiling points

Figure 8 shows that where the elements consist of discrete molecules (the monatomic and diatomic gases and P_4 and S_8) the melting and boiling points are low. This is because only the weak intermolecular van der Waals' forces have to be overcome in melting and boiling the element. The strong, covalent intramolecular forces are unaffected. In the covalent network solids, carbon and silicon, covalent bonds must be broken when melting or boiling takes place – a much more difficult undertaking. Melting and boiling points are therefore much higher (figure 8). Similarly for Group I, II and III elements, their very strong metallic bonds have to be overcome and these elements also have high melting and boiling points compared with covalent molecular elements.

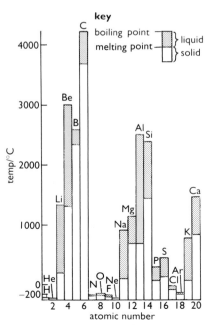

Figure 8 Melting points and boiling points of elements 1 to 20

Conductivity

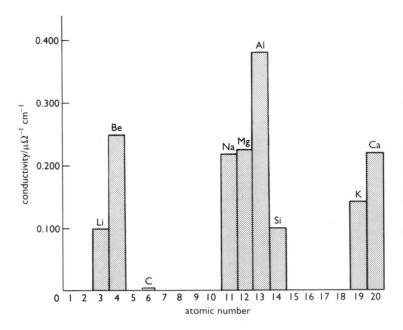

Figure 9 Electrical conductivity of elements 1 to 20

Electrical conductivity is a characteristic property of metals. The conductivity is consistently high for Groups I and II where metallic bonding allows movement of electrons. Aluminium has a similar structure, and high conductivity. Carbon in graphite form has delocalised electrons allowing conduction, although to a lesser degree. Figure 9 shows conductivity values of the first 20 elements.

Covalent atomic radius

Some physical properties of the elements are less easily observed or measured, since they refer to individual atoms. The atomic radius of an element is defined as half the distance between the nuclei of two bonded atoms of the element. Internuclear distances can be measured accurately by X-ray diffraction whereas the boundaries of atoms which are defined by electron orbitals are not clearly observable.

The values for some covalent atomic radii are quoted in table 1 (units picometres i.e. 10^{-12}m). The graph, figure 10, shows their periodic variation.

Li 123	Be 89	B 80	C 77	N 74	O 74	F 72	Ne –	
Na 157	Mg 136	Al 125	Si 117	P 110	S 104	Cl 99	Ar –	increase in value in each column
K 203	Ca 174	Ga 125	Ge 122	As 121	Se 117	Br 114	Kr –	
Rb 216	Sr 191	In 150	Sn 140	Sb 141	Te 137	I 133	Xe –	

decrease in value in ⟶ each row

Table 1

Two quite clear trends are discernable in the table shown. In a horizontal row (period) of the Periodic Table, covalent radii decrease because the atoms being considered all have the same number of occupied energy levels whilst there is an increase of one proton in the nucleus from one element to the next. This increase in the nuclear positive charge exerts an increasing attraction on the electrons resulting in the outer layer (and hence the covalent radius) decreasing in size.

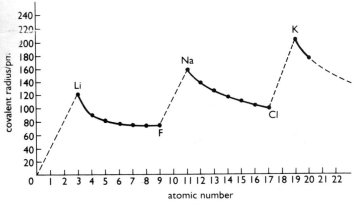

Figure 10 Variation of covalent radius with atomic number for elements 1 to 20

In any vertical column (group) all the elements have the *same number of outer electrons*, but *one more energy level* occupied by electrons in each succeeding element.

Although nuclear charge also increases, its effect is outweighed by the much greater radius of successive electron layers and hence covalent radius increases down a group.

Bond lengths between two atoms in a covalent or polar covalent compound are approximately the sum of the two appropriate covalent radii.

First ionisation energy (or enthalpy)

In the formation of an ionic bond, one important factor is the energy change involved in creating positive ions from neutral isolated atoms, i.e. atoms considered to be in the gaseous state. The change, as with all energy values in chemistry, is measured per mole of atoms and is called the *ionisation energy*. It is an *enthalpy change* and is represented by a ΔH value.

$$Na(g) \rightarrow Na^+(g) + e^- \qquad \Delta H = +502 \, kJmol^{-1}$$

For sodium, 502 kJ of energy are required to remove the first electron from each of one mole of sodium atoms in the gaseous phase. This is properly called the *first ionisation energy of sodium since it is possible to measure the energy required to remove successive electrons from sodium atoms.

The values for some first ionisation energies are quoted in table 2 (units are $kJmol^{-1}$).

Li	Be	B	C	N	O	F	Ne	
526	905	807	1090	1410	1320	1690	2090	
Na	Mg	Al	Si	P	S	Cl	Ar	de-
502	744	584	792	1020	1010	1260	1530	crease down
K	Ca	Ga	Ge	As	Se	Br	Kr	group
425	596	577	762	953	941	1150	1350	
Rb	Sr	In	Sn	Sb	Te	I	Xe	
409	556	556	715	816	870	1020	1170	

——————————overall increase along period ⟶

Table 2 First ionisation energies (kJmol^{-1})

These values are plotted for the first 20 elements in Figure 11.

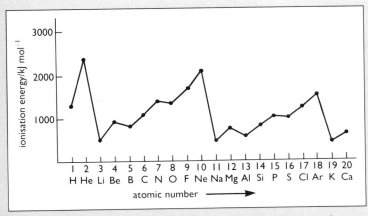

Figure 11 *Variation of first ionisation energy with atomic number for elements 1 to 20*

It is not necessary to explain all the minor features of the graph, but some major points can be made. Firstly in each group of elements, there is a decrease of first ionisation energy as the group descends. The electron is being removed from the outermost layer of electrons. This layer is increasingly distant from the nuclear attraction and hence less energy is required to remove an electron.

In each period, the pattern is less straightforward, but there is an *overall* increase. The electron being removed is in the same layer for any element in the same period e.g. Li – Ne or Na – Ar. As already pointed out, the nuclear charge is increasing along each period, resulting in a contraction in the sizes of the electron orbitals. The outermost electrons are therefore more strongly held and so the energy required to remove them, the ionisation energy, increases along each period.

A further complication arises in connection with the screening effect of electrons in inner orbitals. These inner electrons reduce the attraction of the nucleus on outermost electrons, hence reducing the ionisation energy. The most obvious results of this are seen in the periods K – Kr and Rb – Xe. If the normal group pattern is followed for group III, the first ionisation energy should fall considerably between Al and Ga and between Ga and In, as it does between B and Al. However, the values for Al and Ga are virtually identical and for Ga and In are similar. There are in fact ten transition elements between Ca and Ga, all adding protons to the nucleus whilst electrons are being added to the layer *next to the outermost layer*. The extra protons would increase the ionisation energy of gallium despite the outermost electrons being further from the nucleus, but the extra intervening electrons screen the outermost electrons from the nucleus and the ionisation energy is reduced to be the same as aluminium. A similar effect occurs for indium, there being ten elements between Sr and In, with extra electrons going into an inner layer and giving additional screening.

Finally it is worth noting that within each period the noble gas has the highest value for first ionisation energy. This goes some way to explaining the great stability of filled orbitals and the resistance of the noble gases to formation of compounds. It should be noted however that electrons can be removed from noble gas atoms. If some other step (see the Born-Haber Cycle page 128) can compensate for the energy required then ionic compounds can be made. Xe is the Noble Gas whose compounds were prepared first. (Can you suggest why this was the case?)

BONDING IN COMPOUNDS AND RELATED PROPERTIES

Ionic bonding

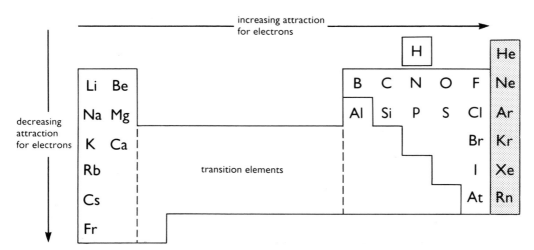

Figure 12 Variation in electron-attracting power

Different elements have different attractions for *bonding* electrons. These attractions are related to nuclear charge and distance of outermost electrons from the nucleus. Two distinct trends are recognisable for the main group elements i.e. excluding the transition elements. Firstly the attraction *increases* along a period from *left to right* up to Group VII and secondly the attraction *decreases down* a group (figure 12).

It follows that fluorine has the greatest attraction for bonding electrons and, in practical terms, caesium has the least attraction.

The greater their difference of attraction for bonding electrons, the less likely are two elements to share electrons, i.e. form covalent bonds. The element with greater attraction is more likely to gain an electron to form a negative ion and the element with smaller attraction to lose an electron to form a positive ion. Ionic bonding results rather than covalent bonding. Elements far apart in the Periodic Table are more likely to form ionic bonds than elements close together. This, in practice, means ionic compounds result from metals combining with non-metals. Typical ionic compounds are sodium fluoride and magnesium oxide. Caesium fluoride is the compound with the greatest degree of ionic bonding.

Structure of ionic compounds

Ionic compounds do not form molecules. Instead the positive and negative ions aggregate into various three dimensional structures called *lattices*. Electrostatic attraction holds the oppositely charged ions together in appropriate numbers so that the total charge is zero. For example, in sodium chloride, there are equal numbers of Na^+ and Cl^- ions, but in calcium fluoride there are twice as many F^- ions as Ca^{2+}. When the lattice forms, energy is released: the lattice energy or enthalpy.

The actual type of lattice depends on the relative numbers of the positive and negative ions and on their relative sizes. If we consider the two compounds sodium chloride and caesium chloride, NaCl and CsCl, we might assume that both would form the same type of lattice, especially since their crystals are both cubic. (Crystal shapes are dependent on the lattice structure.) However their lattices are different as shown by figures 13 and 14.

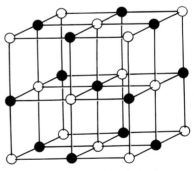

Figure 13 *Sodium chloride lattice*

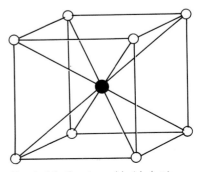

Figure 14 *Caesium chloride lattice*

The difference is caused by the different relative sizes of Na^+ and Cl^-, and of Cs^+ and Cl^-.

Ionic hydrides

The alkali metals will form 'salt-like' hydrides by direct combination with hydrogen. The compounds crystallise in the sodium chloride lattice, and lithium hydride, at least, yields hydrogen at the anode on molten electrolysis.

The hydrides contain the H^- ion, and although its formation is endothermic, its formation is compensated for by the lattice energy, as with the halides.

Compare the following:

$$\tfrac{1}{2}H_2(g) \rightarrow H(g) \qquad \Delta H = +218 \text{ kJ mol}^{-1}$$
$$H(g) + e^- \rightarrow H^-(g) \qquad \Delta H = -72 \text{ kJ mol}^{-1}$$
i.e. $\tfrac{1}{2}H_2(g) \rightarrow H^-(g) \qquad \Delta H = +146 \text{ kJ mol}^{-1}$

$$\tfrac{1}{2}H_2(g) \rightarrow H(g) \qquad \Delta H = +218 \text{ kJ mol}^{-1}$$
$$H(g) \rightarrow H^+(g) + e^- \qquad \Delta H = +1316 \text{ kJ mol}^{-1}$$
i.e. $\tfrac{1}{2}H_2(g) \rightarrow H^+(g) + e^- \qquad \Delta H = +1534 \text{ kJ mol}^{-1}$

In fact the formation of H^- ions is less endothermic than the formation of H^+ ions. The latter exist only in solution where they are stabilised by hydration, with the release of considerable energy.

The hydrides of the alkali metals all react violently with water, evolving hydrogen and forming sodium hydroxide solution.

$$NaH(s) + H_2O(l) \rightarrow Na^+(aq) + OH^-(aq) + H_2(g).$$

Covalent compounds

Most covalent compounds are formed by combinations of non-metallic elements and those encountered previously have been mostly molecular compounds such as methane and carbon dioxide (figure 15).

A number of covalent compounds occur as network structures, of which silicon carbide and silicon dioxide are examples. Their structures are complex and can vary, but it is reasonable to describe that of silicon carbide, SiC, as closely related to that of a diamond type structure.

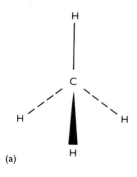

(a)

(b) $O = C = O$

Figure 15

Silicon dioxide, SiO_2, has a hexagonal crystal formed by the bonding of silicon atoms to four oxygen atoms to give SiO_4 tetrahedra. These tetrahedra then link by the sharing of each of their oxygen atoms between two silicon atoms. A helical structure builds up with an overall ratio of two oxygen atoms for each silicon atom.

These network solids have very different properties from ordinary molecular compounds. Thus both silicon carbide and silicon dioxide, or quartz, have very high melting points since melting requires the breaking of strong covalent bonds. They are very hard, although brittle, because of these same strong directional bonds. Silicon carbide, with a network structure similar to diamond, is so hard that it is used as an abrasive in the cutting and grinding surfaces of tools, when it is known as 'carborundum.'

Molecular compounds such as CH_4, CO_2 and SiH_4 (silane) are gaseous at room temperature since the only major forces between the molecules are weak van der Waals' forces. Melting and boiling of these compounds require only the overcoming of these weak van der Waals' forces, whilst the covalent intramolecular forces remain intact.

Polar covalent bonding

Most compounds which are covalent are formed by elements with different electron-attracting abilities, although not so different as those forming ionic bonds. In these compounds, the bonding electrons are not shared equally. The atom with the greater share of electrons will end up with a slight negative charge by comparison with the other atom. For example in hydrogen chloride, the chlorine attracts the bonding electrons more strongly than does the hydrogen. Hydrogen chloride and water can be represented as in figures 16(a) and (b). The symbols δ^+ and δ^- mean 'slightly positive' and 'slightly negative'. Covalent bonds with unequal electron sharing are called polar covalent bonds.

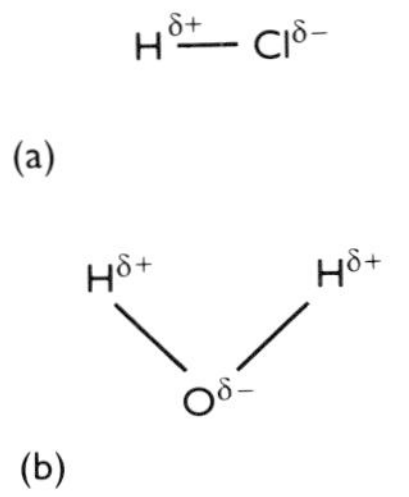

Some molecules containing such polar bonds end up with an overall polarity on the molecule because the bonds are not arranged symmetrically in the molecule. HCl and H_2O are good illustrations of these, as is ammonia (figure 17).

$$H^{\delta+} \!\!-\!\! Cl^{\delta-}$$

(a)

$$H^{\delta+} \qquad H^{\delta+}$$
$$O^{\delta-}$$

(b)

Figure 16

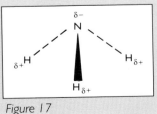

Figure 17

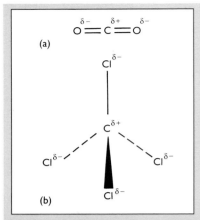

Figure 18

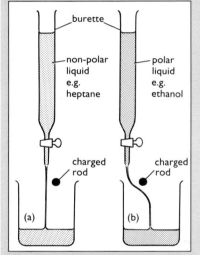

Figure 19 The behaviour of flowing liquids in an electrical field

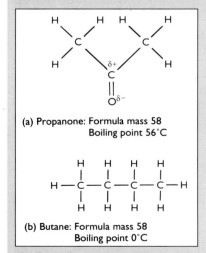

(a) Propanone: Formula mass 58
       Boiling point 56°C

(b) Butane: Formula mass 58
       Boiling point 0°C

Figure 21

Other molecules have a symmetrical arrangement of polar bonds and the polarity cancels out on the molecules as a whole: as in carbon dioxide and tetrachloromethane shown in figures 18(a) and 18(b).

One consequence of these two possibilities is the behaviour of the molecules in an electrical field as illustrated in figure 19. Liquids with molecules which are non-polar behave as in figure 19(a). Liquids with polar bonds behave as in figure 19(b), unless the polarity cancels out, in which case they behave as in figure 19(a).

Heptane has almost non-polar bonds and the molecule is non-polar as a whole. Ethanol has one very polar O—H bond giving the molecule an overall polarity. Chloroform, unlike CCl_4 is polar overall because of the unsymmetrical arrangement of the C—Cl bonds. These structures are shown in figure 20.

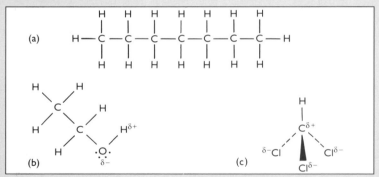

Figure 20

Heptane behaves as in figure 19(a), ethanol and chloroform as in figure 19(b).

Another consequence of molecules having an overall polarity is that their boiling points are higher than those of non-polar molecules of a similar molecular mass. The intermolecular forces are increased. Propanone and butane shown in figure 21 are good examples of this behaviour.

Water as a solvent

Because of its polar nature, water is capable of dissolving other polar and ionic substances. It is a general rule that polar and ionic substances are more likely to dissolve in polar solvents and non-polar substances are more likely to dissolve in non-polar solvents. For example; salt dissolves in water but not in heptane whereas wax dissolves in heptane but not in water.

Hydrogen chloride is very soluble in water. See figure 22 for the mechanism by which it dissolves.

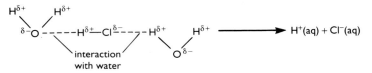

Figure 22 Hydrogen chloride dissolving in water

The dissolving of the hydrogen chloride results in the uneven breaking of the H—Cl bond giving a strongly acidic solution, hydrochloric acid. Similarly ionisation occurs when the other hydrogen halides, HBr and HI are dissolved in water and when pure sulphuric acid, also polar covalent, is dissolved in water. All give rise to strongly acidic solutions, i.e. fully ionised solutions, despite their original structures being polar covalent. If any of the hydrogen halides is dissolved in non-polar toluene, ionisation does not occur and the solutions are not acidic.

Ionic substances dissolve in a similar way, but the ions of course exist in the initial lattice.

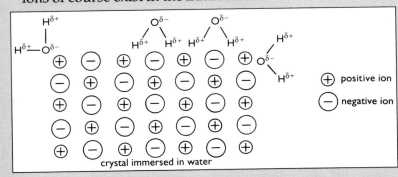

Figure 23 An ionic crystal dissolving in water

The attraction drags ions out of the lattice and they go into solution surrounded by water molecules. The process is illustrated by figures 23 and 24.

Ions surrounded by a layer of water molecules, held by electrostatic attraction, are said to be *hydrated*.

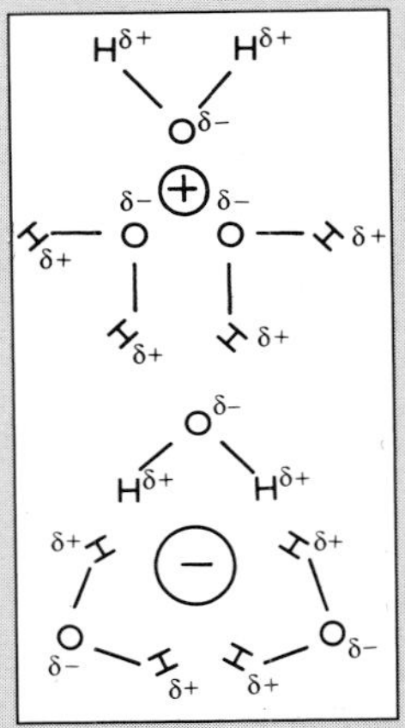

Figure 24 Hydrated ions

Whether an ionic substance will dissolve in water partly depends on the energies associated with breaking up the crystal lattice and with hydrating the ions.

A substance is more likely to dissolve if the energy given out when its ions are hydrated is greater than the energy required to break up the crystal lattice. It must be stressed that this is only one of the factors determining the solubility of a substance.

Anomalous physical properties of some hydrides

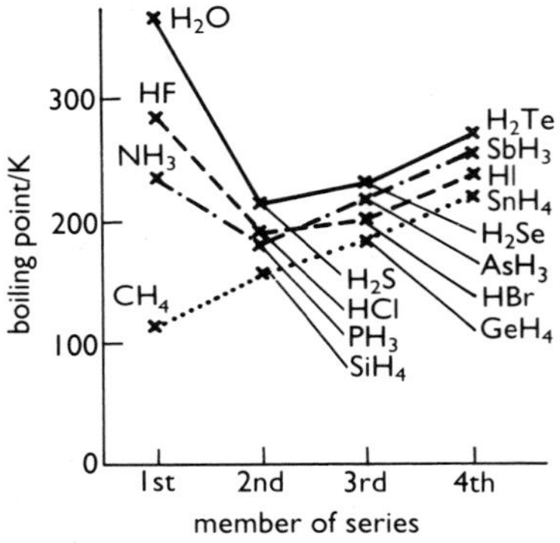

BOILING POINTS

The accompanying graph, figure 25, shows for the Group IV hydrides the expected increase in boiling point with molecular mass. However, in the other three groups, the values of boiling points for NH_3, H_2O and HF (and HCl to some extent) are higher than would be expected for their molecular mass.

These anomalous properties would appear to indicate stronger bonding between the molecules than the expected van der Waals' bonding.

The compounds showing these anomalous properties all contain bonds which are distinctly polar i.e. O—H, N—H, F—H (and Cl—H). These molecules can therefore interact in the fashion shown in figure 26.

Figure 25 Boiling points of hydrides of groups IV, V, VI and VII

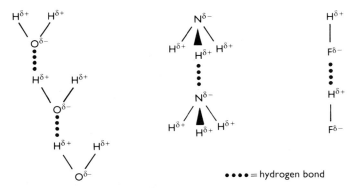

Figure 26 Hydrogen bonding in water, ammonia and hydrogen fluoride

This weak interaction is called *hydrogen bonding* since it occurs only for compounds containing a strongly electron attracting element linked to hydrogen. The pull of electrons away from the hydrogen results in a positive charge located on a small atom, and hence a high positive charge density capable of interacting with the negative end of other molecules.

Hydrogen bonding is slightly stronger than van der Waals' bonding, about 30 kJ mol^{-1} compared with 4 kJ mol^{-1}, but weaker than covalent bonds which are of the order of 450 kJ mol^{-1}.

An important consequence of hydrogen bonding is the unusual way in which water freezes.

As with all liquids, water contracts on cooling, but when it reaches 4°C it begins to expand again, and therefore at its freezing point is less dense than water which is about to freeze (see figure 27). The reason for this is the ordering of molecules into an open lattice, shown in figure 28, as the hydrogen bonds are able to overcome the decreasing thermal motion of the molecules. As a result ice floats in water, seas freeze from the top downwards, allowing fish to survive in unfrozen water beneath (and allowing life to evolve in the sea without interruption) and of course pipes burst when water freezes inside them.

In a biochemical context, hydrogen bonds are responsible for the binding together of the two helices of DNA.

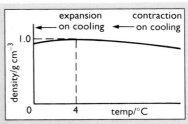

Figure 27 Water: change in density on cooling

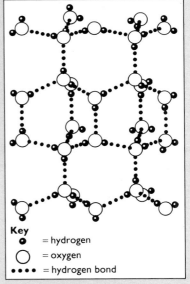

Figure 28 Structure of ice

Properties of oxides

The oxides of most of the elements can be made by direct combination. We have used histograms and graphs earlier in this section to show the variations of some physical properties of the elements with atomic number. Such graphs were used by the German chemist, Lothar Meyer, to arrive at the fundamental idea, in inorganic chemistry, of the Periodic Law virtually at the same time as the better known Russian, Mendeleev. In general terms the law states that, as the elements are studied in order of increasing atomic number, elements which are physically and often chemically similar are seen at regular intervals. These similar elements are elements of the same groups of the Periodic Table and the elements between successive members of Group I are the horizontal rows or 'periods'.

A study of the physical properties of sets of compounds of the elements shows the same periodicity. The following table includes several physical properties of the oxides of the first 20 elements. Plots of melting and boiling point against atomic number will give graphs like those of Lothar Meyer, i.e. elements of the same group occur at similar positions on the 'waves' of the graphs. If their bonding type is considered, similar oxides occur in the same group.

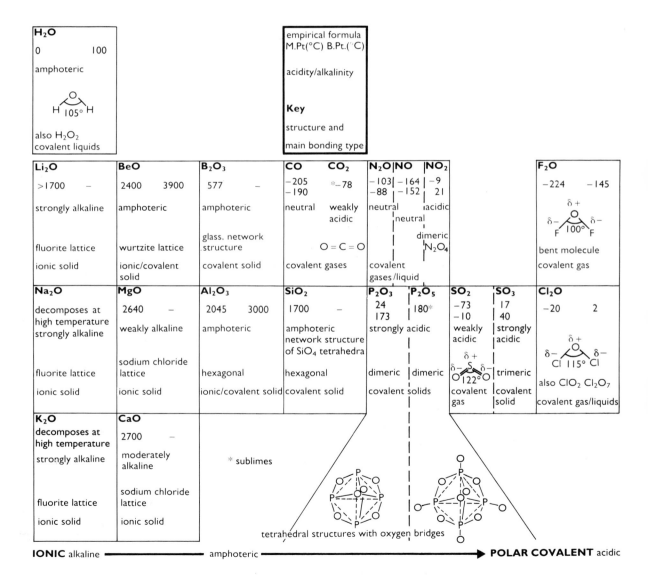

Table 3 Oxides of the first 20 elements

The oxides of Group I, and also magnesium and calcium oxides produce alkaline solutions. For example:

$$Na_2O + H_2O \rightarrow 2Na^+(aq) + 2OH^-(aq)$$
$$MgO + H_2O \rightarrow Mg^{2+}(aq) + 2OH^-(aq)$$

Most metal oxides are however insoluble in water, but dissolve in acid forming salts.

e.g.
$$CuO + H_2SO_4 \rightarrow CuSO_4 + H_2O$$
$$PbO + 2HNO_3 \rightarrow Pb(NO_3)_2 + H_2O$$

The metal oxides are behaving as bases by neutralising the acid.

Many of the oxides of groups V, VI and VII, and carbon dioxide produce acidic solutions.

e.g.
$$SO_2 + H_2O \rightarrow H_2SO_3 \rightleftharpoons 2H^+(aq) + SO_3^{2-}(aq)$$
$$P_2O_5 + 3H_2O \rightarrow 2H_3PO_4 \rightleftharpoons 6H^+(aq) + 2PO_4^{3-}(aq)$$

Some of the oxides e.g. N_2O and CO undergo no change with water or with acid or alkali (neutral oxides). Another group, including the oxides of beryllium, aluminium and silicon, although not soluble in water alone, behave in an amphoteric fashion. Amphotericity is the ability of one substance to behave as an acid in reaction with a base, or as a base in reaction with an acid.

E.g. Aluminium oxide can act as a base with sulphuric acid:

$$Al_2O_3 + 3H_2SO_4 \rightarrow Al_2(SO_4)_3 + 3H_2O$$
(Aluminium sulphate + water)

It can also react as an acid with sodium hydroxide:

$$Al_2O_3 + 2NaOH \rightarrow 2NaAlO_2 + H_2O$$
(Sodium aluminate + water)

These reactions are often difficult to perform with commercial aluminium oxide, but can be carried out with hydrated aluminium oxide, or aluminium hydroxide, precipitated from aluminium sulphate solution by sodium hydroxide solution. The precipitate can be filtered off and will dissolve in dilute acid or in excess sodium hydroxide solution.

Most of these amphoteric oxides are the ones whose structure cannot be clearly described as ionic or covalent, but are intermediate between these types.

111

Chlorides

The bonding present in chlorides varies in a similar manner to that of the oxides, as shown in table 4 for the first twenty elements. As a consequence their physical properties also vary periodically.

The ionic chlorides, and some others, can generally be made by direct combination of the element with chlorine.

e.g.
$$2Na(s) + Cl_2(g) \rightarrow 2NaCl(s)$$
$$Mg(s) + Cl_2(g) \rightarrow MgCl_2(s)$$

The behaviour of chlorides with water is related to their bond type. The ionic chlorides dissolve in water, as described in the section 'Water as a solvent' page 106, and are recovered unchanged on evaporation of the water. Polar covalent chlorides are hydrolysed by reaction with the water and acidic solutions result.

e.g.
$$SiCl_4 + 3H_2O \rightarrow H_2SiO_3 + 4HCl$$
$$PCl_5 + H_2O \rightarrow POCl_3 + 2HCl$$

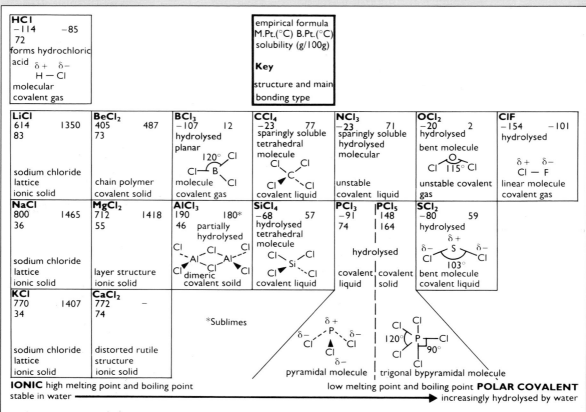

Table 4 Chlorides of the first 20 elements

Summary

| | STRUCTURE TYPE: | |
Ionic	Covalent network	Covalent molecular
High melting point	High melting point	Low melting point
High boiling point	High boiling point	Low boiling point
Strong electrostatic attractions have to be overcome to break up lattice	Strong covalent bonds have to be broken to allow network to break up	Weak van der Waals' forces or hydrogen bonds (also weak) between molecules are all which need to be overcome
Soluble in polar liquids	Normally insoluble since covalent bonds would have to be broken	Normally more soluble in non-polar solvents
Molten compound and aqueous solution both conduct with electrolysis since ions are free to move	Molten material non-conducting since no ions present nor free electrons	Solutions non-conducting unless ionisation can occur, as with HCl in water. Then they may electrolyse

Table 5

SOME ASPECTS OF GROUP VII (HALOGEN) CHEMISTRY

The halogens are the most reactive group of non-metals. They are most commonly found in the Earth's crust in combination with Group I and Group II metals, which are the most reactive groups of metals.

Some data concerning the halogens is shown in table 5 and figures 29 to 32. As described in a previous section, page 95, the halogens all exist as diatomic molecules, the bond lengths being given in figure 2. The covalent bond energies are:

F—F	155 kJ mol^{-1}
Cl—Cl	243 kJ mol^{-1}
Br—Br	194 kJ mol^{-1}
I—I	161 kJ mol^{-1}

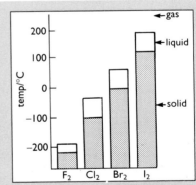

Figure 29 Melting and boiling points of the halogens

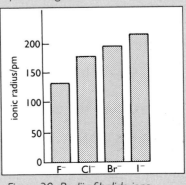

Figure 30 Radii of halide ions

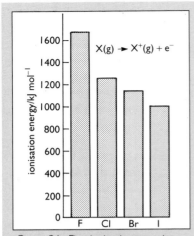

Figure 31 First ionisation energies of halogen atoms

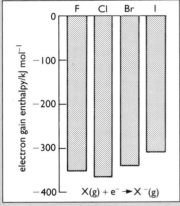

Figure 32 Electron gain enthalpies of halogen atoms

One interesting feature of the halogens' chemistry is their ability to undergo displacement reactions, an ability common amongst the metals.

e.g.

$$Zn(s) + Cu^{2+}(aq) + SO_4^{2-}(aq)$$
$$\rightarrow Cu(s) + Zn^{2+}(aq) + SO_4^{2-}(aq)$$

In general the more reactive metal is oxidised, whilst the less reactive metal's ion is reduced.

$$Zn \rightarrow Zn^{2+} + 2e^- \text{ (oxidation)}$$
$$Cu^{2+} + 2e^- \rightarrow Cu \text{ (reduction)}$$

With the halogens, the following displacement reactions are possible.

$$Cl_2(aq) + 2K^+(aq) + 2I^-(aq) \rightarrow I_2(aq) + 2K^+(aq) + 2Cl^-(aq)$$

$$Cl_2(aq) + 2K^+(aq) + 2Br^-(aq)$$
$$\rightarrow Br_2(aq) + 2K^+(aq) + 2Cl^-(aq)$$

$$Br_2(aq) + 2K^+(aq) + 2I^-(aq) \rightarrow I_2(aq) + 2K^+(aq) + 2Br^-(aq)$$

Note that, as with the SO_4^{2-} ions in the metallic example, the K^+ ions are 'spectator' ions. They are not involved in the reaction.

The reactions can be simplified to:

$$Cl_2(aq) + 2I^-(aq) \rightarrow I_2(aq) + 2Cl^-(aq) \qquad (1)$$

$$Cl_2(aq) + 2Br^-(aq) \rightarrow Br_2(aq) + 2Cl^-(aq) \qquad (2)$$

$$Br_2(aq) + 2I^-(aq) \rightarrow I_2(aq) + 2Br^-(aq) \qquad (3)$$

In each case the smaller halogen molecules are being reduced.

$$Cl_2 + 2e^- \rightarrow 2Cl^- \qquad (1) \text{ and } (2)$$

$$Br_2 + 2e^- \rightarrow 2Br^- \qquad (3)$$

The larger halide ions are being oxidised.

$$2I^- \rightarrow I_2 + 2e^- \qquad (1) \text{ and } (3)$$
$$2Br^- \rightarrow Br_2 + 2e^- \qquad (2)$$

Transfer of electrons in this way can be explained by the attraction for electrons being greater in the small halogen atom, where the outer electrons are in orbitals nearer to the nucleus than in the larger halide ions. Overall the enthalpy changes involved in these electron transfers are exothermic. If the bond energies of the covalent halogen molecules are considered it can be seen that overall the covalent bond changes are endothermic (table 6).

Bond broken	ΔH /kJ mol^{-1}	Bond formed	ΔH /kJ mol^{-1}	Overall ΔH /kJ mol^{-1}
Cl—Cl	+243	I—I	−161	+82
2 Cl—Cl	+243	Br—Br	−194	+49
3 Br—Br	+192	I—I	−161	+31

Table 6

Since the covalent bond changes are energetically unfavourable, the 'redox' or electron transfer factors are presumably dominant in allowing the displacement reactions to take place.

The displacement reactions of the halogens can be used as a test for bromide and iodide ions. To confirm the identity of a suspected bromide or iodide in solution, a solution of chlorine, 'chlorine water', is added followed by addition of 1,1,1–trichloroethane. After shaking and allowing to stand, an orange lower layer (a solution of bromine) confirms the bromide, and a violet lower layer (a solution of iodine) confirms the iodide. Figure 33 illustrates these tests.

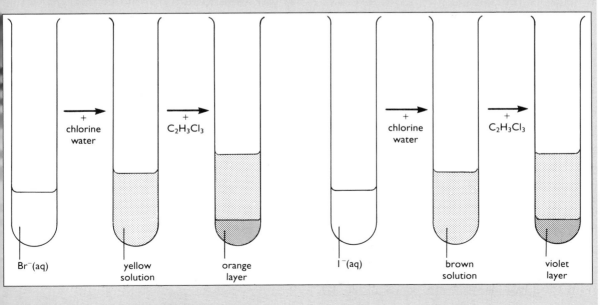

Figure 33 Tests for halide ions in solution

Examples for practice

1. (a) Explain the change in atomic (covalent) radius of the elements
   (i) across the Periodic Table from lithium to fluorine;
   (ii) down Group I from lithium to caesium. (2)
   (b) Which two elements, of all those considered in (a), form the compound with most ionic character. (1)
   (SEB) (Total: 3)

2. (a) Which type of bonding exists in
   (i) sulphur dioxide;
   (ii) silicon dioxide? (1)
   (b) Use the Data Booklet to find the boiling points of these compounds. [PS](1)
   (c) Explain why the boiling point of sulphur dioxide is low. (1)
   (SEB) (Total: 3)

3. A chemist discovered that the same amount of energy was required to remove an electron from an *atom* of xenon as from a *molecule* of oxygen.
   (a) The compound $O_2{}^+PtF_6{}^-$, had already been made. Predict the formula for a similar compound of xenon. [PS](1)
   (b) The first compounds made containing noble gases were xenon compounds. Explain why it is easier to make compounds of xenon than compounds of argon or krypton. (1)
   (SEB) (Total: 2)

4.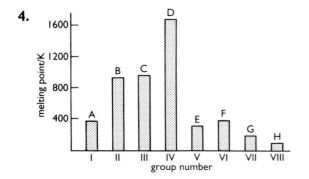

The graph shows the melting points for the elements across a Period in the Periodic Table.
(a) Identify the Period represented by the graph. (1)
(b) The bonding in both elements A and B is metallic. Suggest why the melting point of element B is higher than that of element A. (1)
(c) Elements D and E are both covalently bonded. In terms of structure, account for the large difference in their melting points. (1)
(SEB)(Total: 3)

5. Calcium hydride is melted and electrolysed.
(a) Write the ion-electron equation for the half-reaction occurring at the positive electrode. (1)
(b) What are the products when calcium hydride is added to water? (1)
(Total: 2)

6. You will find the first ionisation energies for the elements in the Data Book.
(a) What trend in first ionisation energies do you observe within the group of halogen elements? [PS](1)
(b) Representing a halogen atom by X, write an equation to show what is happening during the 'first ionisation' process. (1)
(c) Offer an explanation in terms of atomic structure for the trend observed. (2)
(d) Suggest a reason for the lack of ionisation energy data for the element Astatine (At, atomic number 85). (1)
(SEB)(Total: 5)

7. (a) Of the elements of atomic number 3–10 choose one in each case which has a structure you would classify as
   (i) metallic,

(ii) covalent, 'network' type,

(iii) covalent, 'discrete molecules.' (3)

(b) Use the examples you have chosen for each of the types (i) – (iii) and the relevant data to support the following statement:

A noteworthy difference between metallic and non-metallic elements (whether these are of 'network' or 'discrete molecule' type) is that the metals can exist as liquids over a wider range of temperature. [PS](3)

(c) State whether you would expect each of the following to conduct electricity appreciably when connected to a low voltage source:

(i) solid rubidium chloride,

(ii) liquid gallium (element 31),

(iii) liquid nitrogen.

Give your reasons briefly in terms of the type of bonding present. [PS](3)

(d)

Compound	Formula	Molecular weight	Boiling point
ethane	CH_3CH_3	30	$-89°C$
methanol	CH_3OH	32	$64°C$
hydrazine	NH_2NH_2	32	$113°C$
silane	SiH_4	32	$-112°C$

(i) From the information given, which of the compounds in the table above contain hydrogen-bonding in the liquid state? [PS](2)

(ii) Why does hydrogen-bonding affect the boiling point of a substance? (2)

(iii) In the table we have compared substances of similar molecular weight. Why is molecular weight significant in this case? (2)

(SEB)(Total: 15)

8. The following equation shows how bromine can be extracted from sea water.

$$Cl_2(g) + 2Br^-(aq) \rightarrow Br_2(aq) + 2Cl^-(aq)$$

(a) Which type of chemical reaction is represented by this equation? (1)

(b) The graph shows the effect of pH on the yield of bromine obtained.

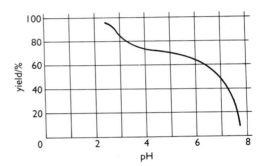

What happens to the yield of bromine as the sea water becomes more acidic? [PS](1)

(c) Would chlorine be a suitable reagent for obtaining fluorine from fluoride ions? Explain your answer. [PS](2)

(SEB)(Total: 4)

6 Thermochemistry

From previous work at Standard Grade you should know and understand the following.

a) A reaction that releases energy is said to the *exothermic*.
b) *Combustion* is the exothermic reaction of a substance with oxygen.
c) A reaction will be exothermic overall if the energy needed to break bonds in the reactants is less than the energy released when new bonds are made in the products.
d) *Neutralisation* occurs when acids react with alkalis or other neutralisers.

From previous work at Higher Grade you should know and understand the following.

a) Potential energy diagrams (unit 1).
b) The *mole* and calculations involving the mole (unit 3).
c) Hydration of ions, solution of ionic compounds and ionisation energies (unit 5).

Throughout this unit you will need to refer to your data book for relevant data on enthalpy changes and bond enthalpies.

EXOTHERMIC AND ENDOTHERMIC REACTIONS

Throughout your study of chemistry you will have often observed that when chemical reactions occur they are accompanied by a significant change in energy. Most of the reactions encountered will have involved a release of energy, usually in the form of heat, and are thus said to be *exothermic*. Examples of such reactions include:

   (i) oxidation of metals and non-metals,
  (ii) combustion of carbon compounds and other fuels,
 (iii) neutralisation of acids by alkalis and reactive metals,
 (iv) displacement of less reactive metals.

Energy may also be released in a chemical reaction in other forms, such as light (e.g. magnesium 'flare' when it burns) or sound (e.g. hydrogen/oxygen and hydrogen/chlorine explosions).

Reactions in which heat is absorbed are said to be *endothermic*. Although less frequent, such reactions do occur, and examples include:

(i) dissolving certain salts in water (e.g. ammonium nitrate, potassium nitrate),

(ii) neutralising ethanoic acid with ammonium carbonate or sodium hydrogencarbonate,

(iii) making a fuel called 'water gas' from steam reacting with hot coke.

i.e.
$$C(s) + H_2O(g) \rightarrow CO(g) + H_2(g)$$
'water gas'

EHTHALPY CHANGE

When an exothermic reaction occurs, the reactants release heat to the surroundings and the products possess less energy as a result. The difference in energy between reactants and products is called the heat of reaction or *enthalpy change*, symbol: ΔH. ΔH values are usually quoted in kilojoules per mole of reactant or product, abbreviated to $kJ\ mol^{-1}$.

Since energy is lost by the reactants in an exothermic reaction, ΔH is said to be negative, as is shown in figure 1 below. In an endothermic reaction the reactants take in heat from the surroundings, so that the products possess more energy than the reactants. Since there is an energy gain by the products, ΔH is positive, as shown in figure 2.

The enthalpy change shown in figure 1 is called the *enthalpy of combustion* of hydrogen, since it is the energy released when one mole of the fuel, i.e. hydrogen, is completely burned.

We can also consider this reaction from the point of view of the product, i.e. water. The enthalpy change is also the *enthalpy of formation* of water, since it is the energy change that occurs when one mole of the compound, water, is formed from its constituent elements, hydrogen and oxygen, in their natural state. Note that the word

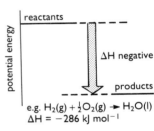

e.g. $H_2(g) + \frac{1}{2}O_2(g) \rightarrow H_2O(l)$
$\Delta H = -286\ kJ\ mol^{-1}$

Figure 1   An exothermic reaction

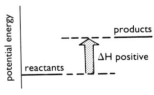

e.g. $C(s) + H_2O(g) \rightarrow CO(g) + H_2(g)$
$\Delta H = +121\ kJ\ mol^{-1}$

Figure 2   An endothermic reaction

'formation' applies strictly in this context to the formation of a compound from its elements. Enthalpy changes of other reactions which produce water, e.g. acid plus alkali or combustion of a hydrocarbon, are *not* the enthalpy of formation of water.

EXPERIMENTAL MEASUREMENT OF ENTHALPY CHANGES

Enthalpy of combustion

The enthalpy of combustion of a simple alkanol can be determined by experiment, using an apparatus like that shown in figure 3.

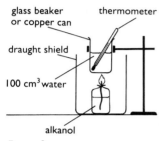

glass beaker or copper can

thermometer

draught shield

100 cm³ water

alkanol

Figure 3

The burner containing the alkanol is weighed before and after burning. The alkanol is allowed to burn until the temperature of the water in the beaker has been raised by, say, 10°C before extinguishing the flame.

The quantity of heat, Q, absorbed by the water in the beaker can be calculated from the relationship,

$$Q = cm\,\Delta T, \text{ where}$$

c is the specific heat capacity of water, 4.18 kJ kg^{-1} K^{-1}
m is the mass of water heated, in kg
ΔT is the change in temperature of the water.

This is a measure of the heat released by the burning alkanol and from this the enthalpy of combustion of the alkanol can be calculated. The method of calculation is shown below using specimen data for the burning of methanol, which gives a result close to the accepted figure given in your Data Book. The result obtained using the above apparatus will be considerably less. It is a useful exercise to consider what the major sources of error might be and how they could be minimised.

Worked example 6.1 Enthalpy of combustion of methanol

Data: Mass of burner + methanol before burning = 53.65 g
Mass of burner + methanol after burning = 53.46 g
Mass of water heated = 100 g   = 0.1 kg
Temperature rise of water   = 10°C

Calculation:

Quantity of heat released	$= cm\,\Delta T\ = 4.18 \times 0.1 \times 10\,kJ$
	$= 4.18\,kJ$

1 mole of methanol weighs 32 g

Mass of methanol burned $= 0.19\,g$

No. of moles of methanol burned, n $= \dfrac{0.19}{32}$

Quantity of heat released per mole $= \dfrac{4.18}{n} \qquad = 4.18 \times \dfrac{32}{0.19}$

$= 704\,kJ$

Enthalpy of combustion of methanol: $\Delta H = -704\,kJ\,mol^{-1}$

Note that, since the reaction is exothermic, it is necessary to insert a negative sign in the final result.

Enthalpy of solution

The enthalpy of solution of a soluble salt can be determined experimentally as illustrated in figure 4. The temperature of the water before adding a weighed amount of solute and the temperature of the final solution are both measured. A thermometer reading to the nearest 0.1 or 0.2 degrees will enable more accurate results to be obtained. The method of calculating enthalpy change is shown below.

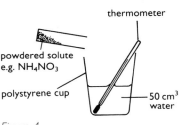

Figure 4

Worked example 6.2 Enthalpy of solution of NH_4NO_3

Data: Mass of solute (ammonium nitrate) $= 1.00\,g$
Mass of water used $= 50\,g \quad = 0.05\,kg$
Temperature of water initially $= 20.4°C$
Temperature of solution $= 18.8°C$

Calculation:

Temperature loss, ΔT $= 1.6°C$

Quantity of heat absorbed $= cm\,\Delta T = 4.18 \times 0.05 \times 1.6\,kJ$

1 mole of NH_4NO_3 weighs 80 g

No. of moles of solute dissolved $= \dfrac{1.00}{80} = 0.0125$

Quantity of heat absorbed per mole $= \dfrac{4.18 \times 0.05 \times 1.6}{0.0125} = 26.8\,kJ$

Enthalpy of solution of ammonium nitrate $\Delta H = +26.8\,kJ\,mol^{-1}$

Since the reaction is endothermic, a positive sign may be inserted in the final result. This is not essential, however. If no sign is given it is assumed to be positive and the reaction endothermic.

BOND ENTHALPIES (BOND ENERGIES)

As was pointed out earlier (unit 1, page 6), a reaction occurring between covalent molecules involves both breaking and making bonds. Energy has to be absorbed to break bonds, hence this is an endothermic process. On the other hand, energy is released when new bonds are formed, hence bond-making is exothermic. Your data book will show that bond enthalpy values vary from one bond to another.

Let us now apply bond enthalpy data to the reaction illustrated in figure 5 and consider the energy changes involved when two moles of hydrogen molecules combine with one mole of oxygen molecules to form two moles of water molecules.

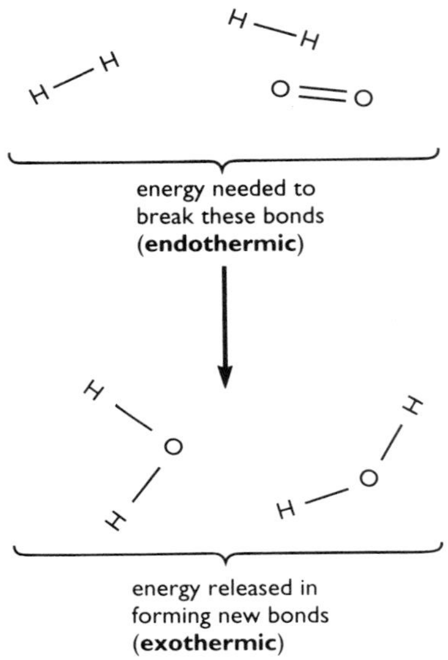

As shown in figure 5, 2 moles of H—H bonds and 1 mole of O=O bonds require to be broken so that 4 moles of H—O bonds can be made in producing 2 moles of water.

energy needed to break these bonds (**endothermic**)

energy released in forming new bonds (**exothermic**)

Figure 5

Bonds broken:

2 moles of H—H bonds require $2 \times 436 \text{ kJ} = 872 \text{ kJ}$
1 mole of O=O bonds requires 497 kJ
Hence, total energy required in bond-breaking is 1369 kJ

Bonds made:

4 moles of H—O bonds releases $4 \times 458 \text{ kJ} = 1832 \text{ kJ}$

Since the total energy released on bond-making is greater than the total energy required for bond-breaking, the overall reaction is exothermic.

$$\Delta H = 1369 - 1832 = -463 \text{ kJ}$$

Thus, for the formation of one mole of water molecules:

$$\Delta H = -231.5 \text{ kJ mol}^{-1}$$

The reaction shown in figure 5 involves the formation of separate water molecules, so that the ΔH value can be regarded as the enthalpy of formation of steam.

$$H_2(g) + \tfrac{1}{2}O_2(g) \rightarrow H_2O(g) \quad \Delta H = -231.5 \text{ kJ mol}^{-1}$$

Note that this value is considerably less than the enthalpy of formation of water quoted earlier in this unit – see figure 1. The difference, about 50 kJ mol^{-1}, is mainly due to the energy released when steam condenses to form water.

Most of the bond enthalpies quoted in your data book are *mean* values, i.e. they are average values obtained by considering various compounds in which those bonds occur. For example, 458 kJ is the average energy needed to break one mole of H—O bonds. These bonds do not only occur in water but also in alcohols, carboxylic acids and carbohydrates.

Comparisons can be made between different examples of covalent bonding. If we consider carbon-to-carbon bonds, we see that the C=C bond enthalpy is much greater than the C—C bond enthalpy, but is significantly less than twice its value. Furthermore, the aromatic C=C bond enthalpy lies between these two values, as pointed out earlier in unit 2, page 30.

The highest bond enthalpy given in your data book is that for N≡N. When you recall how difficult it is to persuade nitrogen gas to react with other elements, it should come as no surprise to find that a very large amount of energy is needed to break down nitrogen molecules into separate atoms.

Enthalpy changes for reactions may be calculated from bond enthalpies provided that all the relevant values are known. The enthalpy change is the algebraic sum of the total energy needed to break bonds in the reactants and the total energy released when making bonds to form the products.

i.e. $\Delta H = \underbrace{\Sigma(\text{Total bond-breaking energy})}_{\text{Endothermic, hence } +}$

$+ \underbrace{\Sigma(\text{Total bond-making energy})}_{\text{Exothermic, hence } -}$

Worked example 6.3

Calculate the enthalpy change for the reaction between hydrogen and chlorine.

$$H_2(g) + Cl_2(g) \rightarrow 2HCl(g)$$

Bonds broken		Bonds made	
H—H	436 kJ	2H—Cl	-2×431 kJ
Cl—Cl	243 kJ		
Total bond-breaking: + 679 kJ		Total bond-making: − 862 kJ	

Hence, the enthalpy change, $\Delta H = 679 + (-862) = -183$ kJ

Since two moles of HCl(g) are formed, the enthalpy of formation of hydrogen chloride will be half this value.

$$\text{i.e. } \Delta H_f = -91.5 \text{ kJ mol}^{-1}$$

Worked example 6.4

Calculate the enthalpy of formation of ethene, C_2H_4.

$$2C(s) + 2H_2(g) \rightarrow C_2H_4(g)$$

This reaction involves the breakdown of two moles of solid carbon (graphite), which as you know has a covalent network structure. A very large number of covalent bonds have to be broken to produce individual atoms of carbon. The process is equivalent to the sublimation of carbon, i.e. the conversion of solid to gas, and the enthalpy change for this is 715 kJ mol^{-1}.

$$\text{i.e. } C(s) \rightarrow C(g) \quad \Delta H = +715 \text{ kJ mol}^{-1}$$

$$2C(s) + 2H_2(g) \rightarrow C_2H_4(g)$$

Bonds broken		Bonds made	
$2C(s) \rightarrow 2C(g)$	2×715 $= 1430$ kJ	C=C	− 607 kJ
2H—H	2×436 $= 872$ kJ	4C—H	-4×414 $= -1656$ kJ
Total bond-breaking: + 2302 kJ		Total bond-making: − 2263 kJ	

Hence, the enthalpy of formation of ethene, $\Delta H_f = 2302 + (-2263) = +39 \text{ kJ mol}^{-1}$

HESS'S LAW

When applying the law of conservation of energy to chemical changes, the following statement can be made. 'The total enthalpy change of a chemical reaction depends only on the chemical nature and physical states of the reactants and products and is independent of any intermediate steps.' This statement is called *Hess's Law*.

This law can be illustrated by the following example (see figure 6), in which alternative routes for converting solid sodium hydroxide into sodium chloride solution are considered. According to Hess's law, the total enthalpy change for each route must be the same.

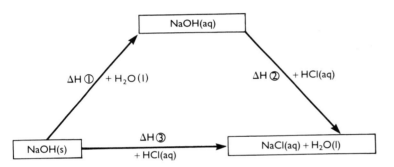

Figure 6

The first route shown in figure 6 involves two steps.

Step 1: Solid NaOH is dissolved in water

$$NaOH(s) + aq \rightarrow NaOH(aq)$$

$$\Delta H① = -43 \text{ kJ mol}^{-1}$$

Step 2: NaOH solution is neutralised by hydrochloric acid

$$NaOH(aq) + HCl(aq) \rightarrow NaCl(aq) + H_2O(l)$$

$$\Delta H② = -57 \text{ kJ mol}^{-1}$$

The second route involves only one step in which the solid NaOH is added directly to hydrochloric acid.

Step 3: $NaOH(s) + HCl(aq) \rightarrow NaCl(aq) + H_2O(l)$

$$\Delta H③ = -100 \text{ kJ mol}^{-1}$$

Hence, $\Delta H① + \Delta H② = \Delta H③$

That Hess's Law is a consequence of the law of conservation of energy can be shown theoretically as follows. If, in the above example, step ③ was readily reversible and that it was found that the sum of ΔH① and ΔH② was greater than ΔH③, it would therefore be possible to create energy by carrying out steps ① and ② and then reversing step ③. This would violate the law of conservation of energy which states that energy cannot be created or destroyed, but can only be converted from one form into another.

APPLICATION OF HESS'S LAW

Hess's Law is important because it enables us to calculate enthalpy changes which are either very difficult or impossible to measure by practical means, for example the enthalpies of formation of hydrocarbons and other carbon compounds.

Worked example 6.5

Calculate the enthalpy of formation of methane.

$$C(s) + 2H_2(g) \rightarrow CH_4(g)$$

Direct combination between carbon and hydrogen does not readily occur and in any event methane is not the only product. Thus, the enthalpy of formation of methane cannot be determined by experiment, but it can be calculated using Hess's Law. Each of the substances in the equation above can be burned and hence an alternative route incorporating their enthalpies of combustion can be devised as shown below.

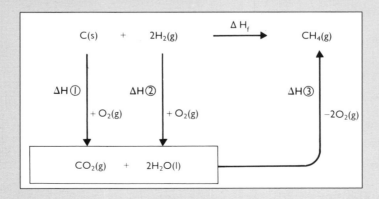

According to Hess's Law, $\Delta H_f = \Delta H$① $+ \Delta H$② $+ \Delta H$③

Reaction	Equation	$\Delta H/kJ$
① Combustion of 1 mole of carbon	$C(s) + O_2(g) \rightarrow CO_2(g)$	-394
② Combustion of 2 moles of hydrogen	$2H_2(g) + O_2(g) \rightarrow 2H_2O(l)$	-572 (i.e. -2×286)
③ *Reverse of combustion of 1 mole of methane*	$CO_2(g) + 2H_2O(l) \rightarrow CH_4(g) + 2O_2(g)$	$+890$
Hence, formation of methane	$C(s) + 2H_2(g) \rightarrow CH_4(g)$	-76

i.e. ΔH_f of methane $= -76\,kJ\,mol^{-1}$

NB: Combustion of methane, $CH_4(g) + 2O_2(g) \rightarrow CO_2(g) + 2H_2O(l)$ $\Delta H = -890\,kJ\,mol^{-1}$

Step ③ is the reverse of this. Hence the numerical value of the enthalpy change for step ③ is the same, but the *sign* must be altered since the direction is reversed.

Worked example 6.6

Calculate the enthalpy of formation of ethyne (acetylene), C_2H_2.

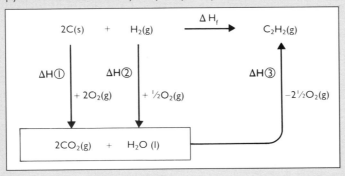

According to Hess's Law, $\Delta H_f = \Delta H① + \Delta H② + \Delta H③$

Reaction	Equation	$\Delta H/kJ$
① Combustion of 2 moles of carbon	$2C(s) + 2O_2(g) \rightarrow 2CO_2(g)$	-788
② Combustion of 1 mole of hydrogen	$H_2(g) + \frac{1}{2}O_2(g) \rightarrow H_2O(l)$	-286
③ *Reverse of combustion of 1 mole of ethyne*	$2CO_2(g) + 2H_2O(l) \rightarrow C_2H_2(g) + 2\frac{1}{2}O_2(g)$	$+1300$
Hence, formation of ethyne	$2C(s) + H_2(g) \rightarrow C_2H_2(g)$	$+226$

i.e. ΔH_f of ethyne $= +226\,kJ\,mol^{-1}$

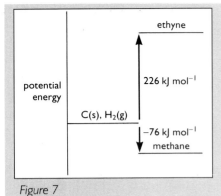

Figure 7

The results of these calculations are compared in figure 7. Since methane has a negative enthalpy of formation, it is more stable than its constituent elements. On the other hand, ethyne has a highly positive enthalpy of formation and consequently it is much less stable than carbon and hydrogen. Ethyne is a gas at room temperature and has a boiling point of $-84°C$. It is liable to explode if liquefied, but it can be safely stored in cylinders if it is dissolved in propanone (acetone) under pressure.

ENTHALPY OF FORMATION OF AN IONIC COMPOUND

In the section on bond enthalpies (page 122) we consider the relevance of the processes of bond-breaking and bond-making in the formation of covalent compounds. Now we shall turn our attention to the formation of an ionic compound from its elements by looking at the component processes which make up the overall reaction. How the enthalpies of these processes relate to the enthalpy of formation of sodium chloride is shown in figure 8 and in the table which follows. The diagram shows what is called a *Born-Haber Cycle* and illustrates how Hess's Law applies to the formation of an ionic compound.

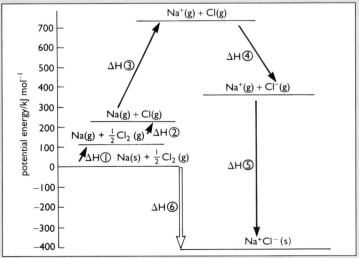

Figure 8

Enthalpy change described	Equation	$\Delta H/kJ$
① Enthalpy of sublimation (or atomisation) of sodium	$Na(s) \rightarrow Na(g)$	$+109$
② Enthalpy of dissociation (or atomisation) of chlorine (half of Cl—Cl bond enthalpy)	$\frac{1}{2}Cl_2(g) \rightarrow Cl(g)$	$+121$
③ The first ionisation energy of sodium	$Na(g) \rightarrow Na^+(g) + e^-$	$+500$
④ The electron gain enthalpy (or electron affinity) of chlorine	$Cl(g) + e^- \rightarrow Cl^-(g)$	-370
⑤ Enthalpy of lattice-forming of sodium chloride	$Na^+(g) + Cl^-(g) \rightarrow Na^+Cl^-(s)$	-771
⑥ Enthalpy of formation of sodium chloride	$Na(s) + \frac{1}{2}Cl_2(g) \rightarrow Na^+Cl^-(s)$	-411

According to Hess's Law,

$$\Delta H⑥ = \Delta H① + \Delta H② + \Delta H③ + \Delta H④ + \Delta H⑤$$

i.e. $\Delta H_f = 109 + 121 + 500 - 370 - 771 = -411 \text{ kJ mol}^{-1}$

Steps ① and ② are endothermic, since they both involve bond-breaking, metallic bonding in step ①, covalent in step ②. Ionisation, that is the removal of an electron to form a positive ion, is also endothermic (step ③), but electron affinity, i.e. the gain of an electron to form a negative ion, is exothermic (step ④). Note that the term ionisation in this context only applies to the formation of positive ions. The enthalpy of forming negative ions is called the electron gain enthalpy or electron affinity. The first ionisation energy of chlorine, 1260 kJ mol^{-1}, is *not* relevant to the present discussion since it is the enthalpy change for the reaction:

$$Cl(g) \rightarrow Cl^+(g) + e^-$$

Although the electron affinity partly compensates for the endothermic step, it can be seen from figure 8 that the main reason why the overall reaction in the formation of sodium chloride is exothermic lies with the highly negative enthalpy of lattice-forming. A large amount of energy is released as separate ions in the gaseous state come together to form the crystal lattice of the solid ionic compound. The energy change for the reverse process is called the enthalpy of lattice-breaking, and is, of course, highly endothermic.

Most ionic compounds have highly negative enthalpies of formation, so they tend to be very stable compounds. This is mainly due to the large amount of energy released when forming the lattice.

SOLUTION OF IONIC COMPOUNDS IN WATER

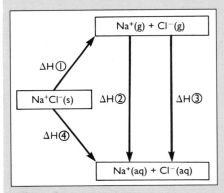

Figure 9

When an ionic compound dissolves in water, two processes occur. The lattice breaks down releasing the ions which then become hydrated by combining with water molecules. This is described in unit 5, page 107 and illustrated in figures 23 and 24 of that unit.

Thus the enthalpy of the solution of a salt or other ionic compound can be regarded as an energy balance between the endothermic process of lattice-breaking and exothermic hydration of ions. This is illustrated by this example (figure 9) in which the solution of sodium chloride in water is considered.

Enthalpy change described	Equation	ΔH/kJ
① Enthalpy of lattice-breaking of sodium chloride	$Na^+Cl^-(s) \rightarrow Na^+(g) + Cl^-(g)$	+771
② Enthalpy of hydration of sodium ions	$Na^+(g) + aq \rightarrow Na^+(aq)$	−405
③ Enthalpy of hydration of chloride ions	$Cl^-(g) + aq \rightarrow Cl^-(aq)$	−362
④ Enthalpy of solution of sodium chloride	$Na^+Cl^-(s) + aq \rightarrow Na^+(aq) + Cl^-(aq)$	+4

According to Hess's Law,

$$\Delta H④ = \Delta H① + \Delta H② + \Delta H③$$

Thus enthalpy of solution of NaCl,

$$\Delta H④ = 771 - 405 - 362 = 4 \text{ kJ mol}^{-1}$$

Although lattice-breaking is highly endothermic, this is almost completely compensated for by the exothermic hydration of ions, so that the overall reaction is slightly endothermic.

Whether an enthalpy of solution is positive or negative will depend on the relevant enthalpies of lattice-breaking and hydration of ions. Many ionic compounds absorb heat when they dissolve in water, but there are also many which release heat, a notable example being sodium hydroxide (see the section on Hess's Law, page 125).

Examples for practice

Refer to worked examples:
6.1 and 6.2 if you need help with questions 1–3,
6.3 and 6.4 if you need help with questions 7–11,
6.5 and 6.6 if you need help with questions 12–14,
and refer to pages 128 to 131 if you need help with questions 15-17.

1. 1.00 g of ethanol was burned and the heat produced warmed 5 litres of water from 20.1°C to 21.5°C. Calculate the enthalpy of combustion of ethanol. (SEB)(4)

2. 0.01 moles of methane were burned and the heat produced warmed 200 cm^3 of water from 15.0°C to 25.5°C. Calculate the enthalpy of combustion of methane. (3)

3. 3.03 g of potassium nitrate was dissolved in 100 cm^3 of water. The temperature of the water fell by 2.5°C. Calculate the enthalpy of solution of this salt. (3)

4. The enthalpy of neutralisation of hydrochloric acid by sodium hydroxide is represented by:

$$HCl(aq) + NaOH(aq) \rightarrow NaCl(aq) + H_2O(l)$$
$$\Delta H = -57.3 \text{ kJ}$$

Write a balanced equation in each case for the partial neutralisation of 1 mole of phosphoric acid (H_3PO_4) by sodium hydroxide when the enthalpy of neutralisation is
(a) −57.3 kJ
(b) −114.6 kJ. (SEB)[PS](2)

5. Using the enthalpies of combustion in the Data Book choose values for three members of each of two homologous series. Use these figures to support the statement: 'There is a regular increase in the enthalpy of combustion as you move up an homologous series. The increase is the similar for all such series.' (SEB)[PS](3)

6. The reaction between hydrazine and hydrogen peroxide can be used for propelling rockets.

$$N_2H_4(l) + 2H_2O_2(l) \rightarrow N_2(g) + 4H_2O(g)$$

$$\Delta H = -685 \text{ kJ mol}^{-1}$$

From the information given in the equation suggest *two* reasons for its suitability.

(SEB)[PS](2)

7. Use the data shown below to calculate:
(a) the average C—Cl bond enthalpy in tetrachloromethane, CCl_4, and (1)
(b) the enthalpy of formation of gaseous tetrachloromethane. (3)

$$CCl_4(g) \rightarrow C(g) + 4Cl(g) \quad \Delta H = 1308 \text{ kJ}$$

$$C(s) \quad \rightarrow C(g) \qquad \Delta H = 715 \text{ kJ}$$

$$Cl_2(g) \quad \rightarrow 2Cl(g) \qquad \Delta H = 243 \text{ kJ}$$

(Total: 4)

8.

Bond	Bond enthalpy/kJ mol^{-1}
N—H	391
N≡N	941
H—H	435

Use the values of bond enthalpy in the table to calculate the enthalpy of formation of 1 mole of ammonia from its elements. Show all your working and indicate clearly whether the reaction is exothermic or endothermic. (SEB) (5)

9. Use the information on bond enthalpies given in your Data Book to calculate the enthalpy of reaction for the addition of bromine vapour to ethene. (3)

10. Using information on bond enthalpies, calculate the enthalpy change for the reaction:

$$CHCl_3(g) + 2HF(g) \rightarrow CHClF_2 + 2HCl(g)$$

(SEB) (5)

11.

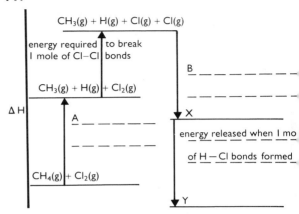

The above diagram, which is *not* to scale, could be part of a calculation to measure ΔH_r for the following reaction:

$$CH_4(g) + Cl_2(g) \rightarrow CH_3Cl(g) + HCl(g)$$

Complete this diagram as follows.
(a) Write statements beside the arrows at A and B describing what each energy change is. (2)
(b) Write the relevant formulae on the lines marked X and Y. (2)
(c) Mark in an arrow labelled 'ΔH_r' for the heat of the reaction. (1)

(SEB)(Total: 5)

12. (a) Write the equations for the formation of benzene, C_6H_6, from its constituent elements. (1)
(b) Use data on enthalpy of combustion from your Data Book to calculate the enthalpy of formation of benzene. (3)
(c) Refer to figure 7 on page 128 and comment on the relative stability of benzene, methane and ethyne. (1)

(Total: 5)

13. (a) The enthalpy of combustion of cyclopropane, C_3H_6, is $-2093 \, kJ\,mol^{-1}$. Use this and relevant data from your Data Book to calculate the enthalpy of formation of cyclopropane. (3)

(b) Compare your answer in (a) to the enthalpy of formation of propane given in your Data Book and decide which is less stable, propane or cyclopropane. (1)

(Total: 3)

(c) Use a molecular model kit to help you predict how C—C bond enthalpies in propane and cyclopropane will compare. Explain your answer. [PS](2)

(Total: 6)

14. (a) Write the equation for the complete hydrogenation of ethyne, C_2H_2, to form ethane. (1)

(b) Use information on enthalpy of combustion given in your Data Book to calculate the enthalpy change for this reaction. (4)

(Total: 5)

15. Rubidium (Rb), an alkali metal, and iodine (I_2), a halogen, are both solid at room temperature.

(a) Write equations to illustrate the following processes:

   (i) sublimation of iodine

   (ii) dissociation of iodine

   (iii) ionisation of iodine

   (iv) electron gain of iodine. (4)

(b) Which process in (a) is exothermic and which one is not required when considering the processes involved in the formation of the ionic compound rubidium iodide? (2)

(c) Write equations for the three other processes needed for the formation of rubidium iodide. (3)

(d) Write equations for the processes involved when rubidium iodide is dissolved in water. (3)

(Total: 12)

16. The energy level diagram below shows the enthalpy changes associated with the formation of solid potassium chloride from its elements in their standard states. Upward arrows indicate endothermic processes and downward arrows indicate exothermic processes. ΔH_1, the enthalpy of formation of potassium chloride, is the net result of all the other enthalpy changes.

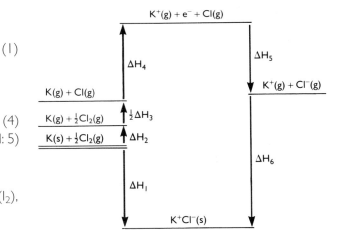

(a) ΔH_1 is the enthalpy of formation of solid potassium chloride and ΔH_6 is the lattice enthalpy of potassium chloride. What names are given to the enthalpy changes ΔH_2, ΔH_3, ΔH_4 and ΔH_5? (2)

(b) Given that $\Delta H_1 = -436 \, kJ\,mol^{-1}$

$$\Delta H_2 = +90 \, kJ\,mol^{-1}$$
$$\Delta H_5 = -356 \, kJ\,mol^{-1}$$

make use of your Data Book to calculate the lattice enthalpy of KCl(s). (4)

(SEB)(Total: 6)

17. (a) Which letters in the table below give names of enthalpy changes which are endothermic? (1)
(b) Which letters represent equations of exothermic reactions? (1)

(c) Match up each letter which *names* an enthalpy change with a letter representing an appropriate equation. (4)
(d) Name the enthalpy change for the reaction shown by the letter *not* used in answering (c). (1)

(Total: 7)

Hydration enthalpy	$Li(g) \rightarrow Li^+(g) + e^-$	Lattice-breaking enthalpy
A	**B**	**C**
$F(g) + e^- \rightarrow F^-(g)$	$Li(s) \rightarrow Li(g)$	$Li^+F^-(s) \rightarrow Li^+(g) + F^-(g)$
D	**E**	**F**
Ionisation enthalpy	$Li^+(g) + aq \rightarrow Li^+(aq)$	Electron gain enthalpy
G	**H**	**I**

7 Chemical equilibrium

From previous work you should know and understand:

a) Acids and alkalis; the importance of H^+ and OH^- ions and the pH scale.
b) Neutralisation and other reactions of acids.
c) Haber process to synthesise ammonia.
d) Factors affecting reaction rates, catalysts (Higher Grade unit 1).
e) How to carry out calculations involving the mole and concentration (Higher Grade unit 3).
f) Enthalpy changes, ΔH and its sign convention, writing equations representing enthalpy changes (unit 6).

[ ] is a recognised abbreviation for 'concentration of' e.g. $[NH_3]$ means concentration of ammonia.

REVERSIBLE REACTIONS

Reversible reactions attain a state of equilibrium when the rate of the forward reaction is equal to the rate of the reverse reaction. Consider a saturated solution containing excess of the undissolved solute, in this case sodium chloride.

$$NaCl(s) \rightleftharpoons Na^+(aq) + Cl^-(aq)$$

In this situation the undissolved sodium chloride is in equilibrium with the dissociated ions. There is constant interchange of ions between the solid and the solution, but the amount of undissolved sodium chloride remains the same. The rate at which ions are dissolving is equal to the rate at which other ions are precipitated.

In bromine water, familiar from tests for unsaturation, there is the following equilibrium:

$$Br_2(l) + H_2O(l) \rightleftharpoons Br^-(aq) + BrO^-(aq) + 2H^+(aq)$$

In each of the above, when the solution is being made up, initially only the forward reactions occur.

$$NaCl(s) \rightarrow Na^+(aq) + Cl^-(aq)$$
$$Br_2(l) + H_2O(l) \rightarrow Br^-(aq) + BrO^-(aq) + 2H^+(aq)$$

The rates of these forward reactions will be related to the high initial concentrations of the solutes. As the reactions proceed, products will be formed. These products form the reactants for the reverse reactions. The reverse reactions can now start. These reactions are initially slow to proceed as *their* reactants are still only in low concentration.

$$i.e.\ Na^+(aq) + Cl^-(aq) \rightarrow NaCl(s)$$
$$Br^-(aq) + BrO^-(aq) + 2H^+(aq) \rightarrow Br_2(l) + H_2O(l)$$

The rates of the forward reactions will decrease as their reactants are consumed, and the rates of the reverse reactions will increase as their reactants increase in concentration.

Eventually the rates of the forward and reverse reactions will be the same, and equilibrium is attained.

It is important to realise, however, that the reaction does *not* stop when equilibrium is attained. When a saturated solution of a salt such as NaCl is formed, an equilibrium is set up in which as many ions are passing into solution as are being redeposited on the solid crystals, i.e. the rate of solution equals the rate of precipitation. At equilibrium these processes do not cease. For this reason, chemical equilibrium is described as being dynamic.

It is also important to note that when equilibrium is reached this does not imply that the equilibrium mixture consists of 50% reactants and 50% products. This will only very rarely be the case. The actual position of equilibrium can be influenced by a number of factors as we shall see later in this chapter.

Under similar conditions, the same equilibrium can be arrived at from two different starting points. This can be shown (figure 1) using the fact that iodine is soluble in trichloroethane $C_2H_3Cl_3$ and also in aqueous potassium iodide solution. Tubes X and Z represent the two starting positions. In X iodine is dissolved in $C_2H_3Cl_3$ only and in Z it is dissolved in KI solution only. Tube Y represents the equilibrium mixture which is obtained. Equilibrium can be attained quickly by shaking the tubes or slowly by allowing them to stand. Many reactions

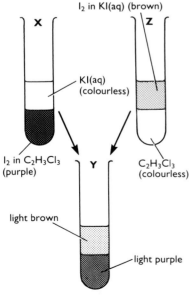

Figure 1 Equilibrium can be reached from either direction

appear to be irreversible, e.g. neutralisation of a strong acid and strong base or precipitation such as

$$Ag^+(aq) + Cl^-(aq) \rightarrow AgCl(s)$$

However, all reactions are, in fact, reversible to at least some extent. We can say, that in such reactions the equilibrium lies so far in one direction that for practical purposes they can be considered as having gone to completion.

CHANGING THE POSITION OF EQUILIBRIUM

We shall now consider the factors which can alter the position of equilibrium in a reversible reaction. Equilibrium is reached when the opposing reactions occur at an equal rate. Hence, we should expect that any condition which changes the rate of one reaction more than the other should change the position of equilibrium, i.e. the relative proportions of reactants and products in the mixture.

This section deals with the influence of changing the concentration, the pressure and the temperature on the equilibrium position. The effect of these changes can be summarised by Le Chatelier's Principle which states that:

'If a system at equilibrium is subjected to any change, the system readjusts itself to try and counteract the applied change.'

Note that this statement *only* refers to reversible reactions which have reached equilibrium.

Changing the concentration

Let us consider the following reaction at equilibrium

$$A + B \rightleftharpoons C + D$$

An increase in the concentration of A (or B) will speed up the forward reaction, thus increasing the concentration of C and D until a new equilibrium is obtained. A similar effect can be achieved by reducing the concentration of C (or D) in some way. These results agree with Le Chatelier's Principle, since the equilibrium has moved to

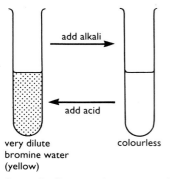

very dilute
bromine water
(yellow)

colourless

Figure 2 Changing the position of an equilibrium: using bromine water

the right to counteract the applied change. The following reactions can be used to illustrate these points.

Bromine water: Bromine dissolves in water forming a red-brown solution which contains a mixture of Br_2 molecules (responsible for the colour), H_2O molecules, H^+, Br^- and BrO^- ions as shown in the equation.

$$Br_2(l) + H_2O(l) \rightleftharpoons 2H^+(aq) + Br^-(aq) + BrO^-(aq)$$

The equilibrium position can be adjusted as shown in figure 2. The addition of OH^- ions removes H^+ ions to form water and the equilibrium shifts to the right. Adding H^+ ions moves the equilibrium back to the left.

Iron(III) ions + thiocyanate ions (CNS^-): When separate solutions containing iron(III) ions and thiocyanate ions respectively are mixed, a deep blood-red solution is formed due to the presence of complex ions such as $[FeCNS]^{2+}$. This reaction is reversible.

$$\underset{\text{pale yellow}}{Fe^{3+}(aq)} + \underset{\text{colourless}}{CNS^-(aq)} \rightleftharpoons \underset{\text{red}}{[FeCNS]^{2+}(aq)}$$

The intensity of the colour may be taken as an indication of the position of equilibrium. Some of the blood-red solution is diluted until an orange colour is obtained, and this solution is poured into four test tubes till each is half-full. Tube A is kept for reference; crystals of iron(III) chloride, potassium thiocyanate and sodium chloride are added to tubes B, C and D respectively. The results are shown in figure 3.

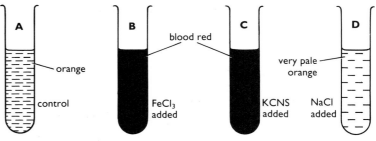

Figure 3 Changing the position of an equilibrium: using iron (III) thiocyanate ions

An increase in the concentration of Fe^{3+} ions or CNS^- ions shifts the equilibrium to the right and results in the formation of more complex ions. The addition of NaCl removes Fe^{3+} ions due to complex formation with Cl^- ions and the equilibrium shifts to the left to compensate.

Changing the temperature

In a reversible reaction, if the forward reaction is exothermic, then the reverse reaction must, of course, be endothermic. If a system at equilibrium is subjected to a change in temperature, the equilibrium position will adjust itself to counteract the applied change, according to Le Chatelier's Principle. Thus, a rise in temperature will favour the reaction which absorbs heat, i.e. the endothermic process, and a fall in temperature will favour the exothermic reaction. This can be seen in the following examples.

Nitrogen dioxide: Brown fumes of nitrogen dioxide are formed when most metal nitrates are decomposed thermally or when copper is added to concentrated nitric acid. The gas produced is, in fact, an equilibrium mixture of nitrogen dioxide, NO_2 (a dark brown gas) and dinitrogen tetroxide, N_2O_4 (a colourless gas). This is represented in the following equation. The forward reaction is endothermic.

$$N_2O_4(g) \rightleftharpoons 2NO_2(g)$$
colourless   dark brown

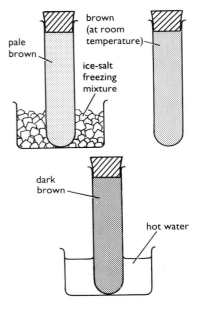

Figure 4   Equilibrium and temperature

Figure 4 illustrates the results obtained on subjecting samples of this gas mixture to different temperature conditions. An increase in temperature favours the endothermic reaction and so the proportion of NO_2 increases and the gas mixture becomes darker in colour. A drop in temperature favours the exothermic reaction and, hence, the gas mixture lightens in colour.

Changing the pressure

The pressure exerted by a gas is caused by the freely moving molecules bombarding the walls of the containing vessel. An increase in the number of molecules will be accompanied by an increase in pressure, the size of the container being kept constant. The effect of changes in pressure on a system involving gases is equivalent to the effect of changes in concentration on a system in solution.

The $N_2O_4-NO_2$ system is a suitable example to study in this connection.

$$N_2O_4(g) \rightleftharpoons 2\,NO_2(g)$$
I mole   2 moles
I volume   2 volumes (at the same T, P)

An increase in pressure will cause the system to re-adjust to counteract this effect, i.e. it will attempt to reduce the pressure within the system. Thus, the equilibrium will adjust to the left, forming more N_2O_4 molecules and reducing the number of molecules per unit volume. A suitable apparatus for the study of this effect is shown in figure 5.

The results are shown in table 1.

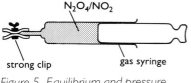

N_2O_4/NO_2

strong clip   gas syringe

Figure 5 Equilibrium and pressure

Applied pressure change	Initial colour change	Final colour change
Increase (plunger in)	Darkens due to compression	Lightens as equilibrium shifts to the left
Decrease (plunger out)	Lightens due to expansion	Darkens as equilibrium shifts to the right

Table 1 (see note opposite*)

Generally in a reversible reaction involving a gas or gases at equilibrium, an increase in pressure will cause the equilibrium to shift in the direction which results in a decrease in the number of gaseous molecules. In a system in which there is no overall change in the total number of gaseous molecules changes in pressure will have no effect on the equilibrium position, e.g.

$$CO(g) + H_2O(g) \rightleftharpoons CO_2(g) + H_2(g)$$
I mole   I mole   I mole   I mole

Catalysts and equilibrium

A catalyst speeds up a reaction by lowering the activation energy. However, in a reversible reaction it reduces the activation energy for both the forward reaction and the reverse reaction by the same amount, as shown in figure 6.

Thus, a catalyst speeds up both reactions to the same extent and does not alter the position of equilibrium. The use of a catalyst does not result in an increased yield of product. The advantage of using a catalyst in a reversible reaction is that it

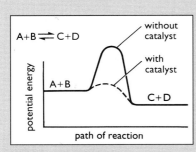

$A+B \rightleftharpoons C+D$

without catalyst

with catalyst

potential energy

A+B

C+D

path of reaction

Figure 6 Potential energy: catalysed and uncatalysed reactions

enables equilibrium to be reached more rapidly than without.

* Authors' note: Teachers may wish to consult *School Science Review* 1978, 211, **60**, 309 for an alternative explanation of the changes observed in the NO_2–N_2O_4 system.

Summary

Change applied	Effect on equilibrium position
Concentration	
Addition of reactant or removal of product	Equilibrium shifts to the right
Addition of product or removal of reactant	Equilibrium shifts to the left
Temperature	
Increase	Shifts in direction of endothermic reaction
Decrease	Shifts in direction of exothermic reaction
Pressure	
Increase	Shifts in direction which reduces the number of molecules in gas phase
Decrease	Shifts in direction which increases the number of molecules in the gas phase
Catalyst	No effect on equilibrium position; equilibrium more rapidly attained

Table 2

EQUILIBRIUM AND INDUSTRIAL REACTIONS

In the Haber process to synthesise ammonia, if a closed reaction vessel is used, an equilibrium is set up:

$$N_2(g) + 3H_2(g) \rightleftharpoons 2NH_3(g)$$

When the rates of the forward and reverse reactions are equal then equilibrium is reached. The same equilibrium is eventually reached whether starting from the nitrogen and hydrogen ('reactant') side or from the ammonia ('product') side. This is a general rule with any reversible reaction.

At equilibrium, the concentrations of reactants and products remain constant, but not necessarily equal. The relative concentrations of reactants and products can be affected by altering the conditions under which the reaction is taking place. This is illustrated in table 3 using the reaction $N_2(g) + 3H_2(g) \rightleftharpoons 2NH_3(g)$.

New conditions	Equilibrium change	Explanation
Increase pressure	To right, $[NH_3]$ increases	Forward direction involves a decrease in number of moles of gas (4 moles → 2 moles) and hence a decrease in volume. Decrease in volume is assisted by increase in pressure
Decrease pressure	To left, $[NH_3]$ decreases	Reverse direction involves an increase in number of moles of gas and hence in volume, assisted by reduced pressure
Increase temperature	To left, $[NH_3]$ decreases	Increasing temperature involves increasing energy of system. The reverse reaction is endothermic and will be assisted by providing energy
Decrease temperature	To right, $[NH_3]$ increases	Decreasing temperature removes energy from system, making reverse endothermic reaction less favourable, less NH_3 splits up
Catalyst	No change	Both forward and reverse reactions are accelerated. The same equilibrium is reached more rapidly

Table 3

In most industrial situations a continuous process is used rather than a small-scale 'batch' process. This means that a true equilibrium, which requires a closed system, is not achieved.

In the Haber process, which is operated continuously, the gases do not have time to reach equilibrium in the catalyst chamber, and the percentage conversion of nitrogen and hydrogen to ammonia is quite low. However, by recycling unreacted nitrogen and hydrogen the overall conversion of nitrogen and hydrogen to make ammonia is very efficient.

In practice the operating conditions for most industrial processes involve compromises amongst yield, construction and maintenance costs, catalyst life and catalyst activity. The following examples illustrate some of these considerations for the Haber process.

$$N_2(g) + 3H_2(g) \rightleftharpoons 2NH_3(g) \text{ forward reaction}$$
$$\qquad\qquad\qquad\qquad\qquad\qquad \text{is exothermic}$$

4 vol   2 vol

The conditions for maximum yield are: low temperature, high pressure. Figure 7 shows the percentage of NH_3 in equilibrium when reacting nitrogen and hydrogen in a 1:3 mixture by volume at different temperatures and pressures.

The lower the temperature is, the higher the percentage of NH_3, but the slower the reaction. The higher the pressure the higher the percentage of ammonia, but the greater the cost of equipment both in outlay and maintenance.

Operating conditions: 400–500°C; high pressure, 200–1000 atmospheres, iron catalyst. The ammonia is condensed on cooling and unreacted nitrogen and hydrogen are recycled.

The above example illustrates the compromises which must be made in choosing the operating conditions for a particular industrial process. The actual process chosen to manufacture a product will itself be decided by consideration of factors including the availability of raw materials, the cost of these materials and of energy, the yield of the product and the marketability of by-products. Increasingly, 'green' factors are being taken into consideration. Processes which were economically viable when regulations on pollution were less stringent may now become uneconomic because of new regulations. Some may even be impossible to 'clean up' sufficiently to allow them to continue.

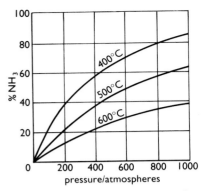

Figure 7 *Haber process: variation of yield with pressure and temperature*

METAL/WATER REACTIONS

In water, some ionisation occurs:

$$H_2O(l) \rightleftharpoons H^+(aq) + OH^-(aq)$$

The ionisation is very slight, only a ten millionth of a mole per litre of water splitting up, to give equal concentrations of H^+ and OH^- ions. Despite the low concentrations of H^+, some reactive metals dissolve in water, forming hydrogen and an alkaline solution. As the few ions initially in the water would result in very little metal dissolving, there must be continuing ionisation of the water. In fact the metal reacts as shown:

$$2Na(s) + 2H^+(aq) \rightarrow 2Na^+(aq) + H_2(g)$$

The H^+ ions are removed from their equilibrium with OH^- ions and water molecules. As a consequence, the equilibrium is disturbed, and shifts to the right, forming more H^+ (and OH^-) ions:

$$H_2O(l) \rightarrow H^+(aq) + OH^-(aq)$$

Eventually enough H^+ ions are produced to dissolve the metal, an equivalent quantity of hydrogen is obtained and a solution of alkaline metal hydroxide is produced since there is now an excess of OH^- ions in the solution.

pH VALUES

The concentration of hydrogen ions in solution is measured in pH units. pH stands for the negative logarithm (to base 10) of the hydrogen ion concentration.
$$pH = -\log_{10} [H^+(aq)]$$
(The symbol 'M' is often used as an abbreviation for moles l^{-1}. Square brackets [ ] denote concentrations of the relevant substance in moles l^{-1}.)

pH and hydrogen ion concentrations $[H^+]$ can be related as in table 4.

$[H^+]$ moles l^{-1}	$\log_{10}[H^+]$	pH($-\log_{10}[H^+]$)
1 (M)	0	0
$\frac{1}{10}$ (10^{-1}M)	-1	1
$\frac{1}{100}$ (10^{-2}M)	-2	2
$\frac{1}{1000}$ (10^{-3}M)	-3	3
$\frac{1}{10^7}$ (10^{-7}M)	-7	7
$\frac{1}{10^{14}}$ (10^{-14}M)	-14	14

Table 4

The pH scale is, of course, a continuous scale with values ranging from less than zero to more than 14. (A concentration of more than 1 mole l^{-1} of H^+ ions will give a positive $\log_{10}[H^+]$ and hence a negative pH value).

For water which ionises, as described above, to reach an equilibrium:

$$H_2O(l) \rightleftharpoons H^+(aq) + OH^-(aq)$$

The equilibrium concentration of both H^+ and OH^- ions is 10^{-7} moles 1^{-1} at 25°C.

i.e. $[H^+] = 10^{-7}M$, pH $= 7$.
If $[H^+] = [OH^-] = 10^{-7}$ mol 1^{-1}.
then $[H^+][OH^-] = 10^{-7} \times 10^{-7}$ mol^2 $1^{-2} = 10^{-14}$ mol^2 1^{-2}

This value is called the ionic product of water.
The equilibrium for the ionisation of water always exists in aqueous solutions.

i.e. $\qquad\qquad H_2O(l) \rightleftharpoons H^+(aq) + OH^-(aq)$

If the solution is acidic, i.e. there is an excess of H^+ ions, then the equilibrium adjusts to the left, some of the excess H^+ ions combining with some of the OH^- ions from water. The ionic product remains 10^{-14} moles^2 1^{-2}. Similarly excess OH^- in an alkaline solution combine with H^+ ions from water, maintaining the ionic product at 10^{-14} moles^2 1^{-2}.

It follows that we can calculate $[H^+]$, pH, $[OH^-]$ for acidic and alkaline solutions using the basic relationship:

$$[H^+][OH^-] = 10^{-14} \text{ moles}^2 \, 1^{-2}$$

From which we derive:

$$[H^+] = \frac{10^{-14}}{[OH^-]} \text{ mol } 1^{-1}$$

$$\text{and } [OH^-] = \frac{10^{-14}}{[H^+]} \text{ mol } 1^{-1}$$

Worked example 7.1

What is the concentration of OH^- ions in a 0.01 M solution of HCl?

$[H^+] \quad = 10^{-2}$ m for a 0.01 M solution of HCl.

$$[OH^-] = \frac{10^{-14}}{[H^+]} = \frac{10^{-14}}{10^{-2}} = 10^{-12}M$$

Worked example 7.2

What is the concentration of H^+ ions in a 0.1 M solution of NaOH?

$[OH^-] = 10^{-1}$ M for a 0.1 M solution of NaOH.

$$[H^+] = \frac{10^{-14}}{[OH^-]} = \frac{10^{-14}}{10^{-1}} = 10^{-13} M$$

Worked example 7.3

What is the pH of a solution of 0.1 M NaOH?

As in 7.2 above, $[H^+] = 10^{-13}$ mol l^{-1}

$$pH = -\log[H^+] = 13$$

Similar calculations show that for a strong acid like HCl and a strong alkali like NaOH, the concentration of the solution can be directly related to pH.

HCl: Concentration/mol l^{-1}	1	10^{-1}	10^{-2}	10^{-3}	10^{-4}	10^{-5}	10^{-6}	10^{-7}
pH	0	1	2	3	4	5	6	7
NaOH: Concentration/mol l^{-1}	1	10^{-1}	10^{-2}	10^{-3}	10^{-4}	10^{-5}	10^{-6}	10^{-7}
pH	14	13	12	11	10	9	8	7

Values of pH for solutions which have concentrations other than $M \times 10^x$, where x is an integer, can be estimated as follows.

Worked example 7.4

Estimate the pH of 0.2 M HCl.

$$[H^+] = 0.2 \text{ mol } l^{-1} = 2 \times 10^{-1} \text{ mol } l^{-1}$$

HCl which is 10^{-1} mol l^{-1} has a pH of 1.
HCl which is 1 mol^{-1}, i.e. 10^0 mol l^{-1}, has a pH of 0.
Thus, 0.2 M HCl will have a pH slightly less than 1.

Worked example 7.5

Estimate the pH of 0.0125M HCl.

$$[H^+] = 0.0125 \text{ mol l}^{-1} = 1.25 \times 10^{-2} \text{ mol l}^{-1}$$

HCl which is 10^{-2} mol l^{-1} has a pH of 2.
HCl which is 10^{-1} mol l^{-1} has a pH of 1.
Thus, 0.0125 M HCl will have a pH slightly below 2.

Worked example 7.6

Estimate the pH of 5 M HCl.

$$[H^+] = 5 \text{ mol l}^{-1}$$

HCl which is 1 mol^{-1} has a pH of 0.
Thus, HCl which is 5 mol l^{-1} has a pH less than 0, i.e. it has a negative value.

Worked example 7.7

Estimate the pH of 5 M NaOH.

$$[OH^-] = 5 \text{ mol l}^{-1} = 5 \times 10^0 \text{ mol l}^{-1}$$

NaOH which is 1 mol l^{-1}, i.e. 10^0 mol l^{-1} has a pH of 14,

since $[OH^-] = 10^0$ mol l^{-1}, and $[H^+] = \dfrac{10^{-14}}{10^0} = 10^{-14}$

Thus, NaOH which is 5 mol l^{-1} has a pH greater than 14.

It can be seen that the pH scale extends below zero and above 14, however the scale is limited by the maximum concentration of H^+ and OH^- that can be achieved owing to the finite solubilities of acids and alkalis.

STRONG AND WEAK ACIDS AND ALKALIS

In the previous calculations, it was assumed that for solutions of hydrochloric acid and sodium hydroxide the $[H^+]$ and $[OH^-]$ were equal to the nominal concentrations of the solutions. This assumption is justified only for strong acids and alkalis, i.e. acids and alkalis that dissociate completely into ions in solutions.

e.g. $$HCl(aq) \rightarrow H^+(aq) + Cl^-(aq)$$

Strong acids include HCl, HNO_3 and H_2SO_4. For the last named, pH calculations must take note of its production of more than one mole of hydrogen ions per mole of solute:

$$H_2SO_4(aq) \rightarrow 2H^+(aq) + SO_4{}^{2-}(aq)$$

Hence the pH of 0.1 M H_2SO_4 is estimated as follows:

$$[H^+] = 0.2 \text{ mol } l^{-1} = 2 \times 10^{-1} \text{ mol } l^{-1}$$
pH is between 1 and 0
Actual value $= 0.699$

Strong alkalis include NaOH and KOH. Other acids and alkalis dissociate only partially into ions in solution, i.e. an equilibrium exists between the ions and undissociated molecules. For example, for ethanoic acid and ammonium hydroxide solutions:

$$CH_3COOH \rightleftharpoons CH_3COO^-(aq) + H^+(aq)$$
$$NH_3 + H_2O \rightleftharpoons NH_4{}^{+4}(aq) + OH^-(aq)$$

The equilibrium will move to the right with increasing dilution i.e. dissociation is greater, or the degree of ionisation is greater with increasing dilution.

Such incompletely dissociated acids and alkalis are called weak acids and alkalis. (Note that 'strong' and 'weak' refer to the inherent ability of acids and alkalis to ionise. These words should not be used to refer to differences in concentration of solutions where 'concentrated' and 'dilute' are the only permissible terms.)

Solutions of strong and weak acids differ in pH, conductivity and reaction rates since their hydrogen ion concentrations are different. Solutions should be equimolar for a fair comparison.

equimolar for a fair comparison.

For 0.1 M HCl and 0.1 M CH_3COOH, these differences can be summed up in table 5.

	0.1 M HCl	0.1 M CH_3COOH
$[H^+]$	0.1 mol l^{-1}	0.0013 mol l^{-1}
pH	1	2.88
Conductivity	high	low
Rate of reaction with Mg	fast	slow
Rate of reaction with $CaCO_3$	fast	slow

Table 5

It should be clear however, since the undissociated molecules of weak acids are in equilibrium with their ions, that as a reaction proceeds consuming H^+ ions the equilibrium shifts in favour of more dissociation until eventually all the molecules are dissociated. Thus eventually the same amount of base is required to neutralise a certain volume of either 0.1 M HCl or 0.1 M CH_3COOH. Hence the stoichiometry of a neutralisation reaction is the same:

$$NaOH + HCl \rightarrow NaCl + H_2O$$
$$NaOH + CH_3COOH \rightarrow CH_3COONa + H_2O$$

1 mole acid $\equiv$ 1 mole alkali in each case.

Similar factors apply to solutions of strong and weak alkalis as shown in table 6.

	0.1 M NaOH	0.1 M NH_3
$[OH^-]$	0.1 mol l^{-1}	0.0013 mol l^{-1}
pH	13	11–12
Conductivity	high	low

Table 6

Again the weak alkali will dissociate further as its OH^- ions react with acids. Eventually it will dissociate fully so that a certain volume of either 0.1 M NaOH or 0.1 M NH_3 will eventually neutralise the same quantity of acid.

i.e.
$$NaOH + HCl \rightarrow NaCl + H_2O$$
$$NH_4OH + HCl \rightarrow NH_4Cl + H_2O$$

1 mole alkali $\equiv$ 1 mole acid in each case.

THE INFLUENCE OF STRUCTURE ON ACID AND ALKALI STRENGTHS

The commonest weak acids are the carboxylic acids containing the group:

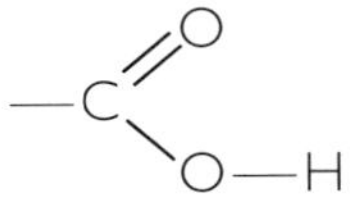

One example is ethanoic acid, with the following structure:

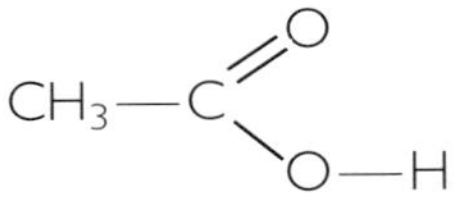

These compounds ionise to a limited degree by the separation of a hydrogen ion from the carboxyl group:

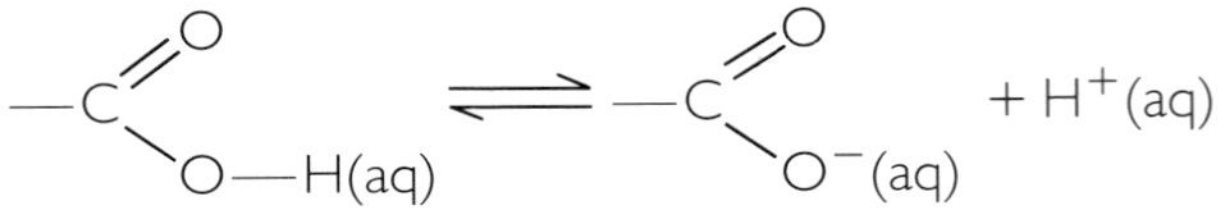

The ionisation is assisted by the polarisation of the covalent bonds within the carboxyl groups as shown in figure 8.

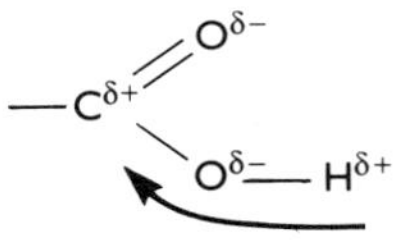

Figure 8

This results in electrons being pulled away from the hydrogen in the direction of the arrow, so weakening the O—H bond which then splits unevenly to leave H^+ ions.

Many of these weak acids are present in fruit juices and are responsible for their characteristic sour taste owing to the moderate concentration of hydrogen ions. Typical examples of such acids are shown in table 7.

Name of acid	Occurrence	Structural formula
Citric acid	In oranges and lemons	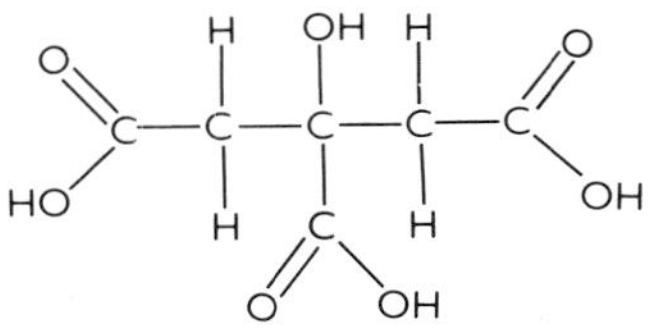
Malic acid	In apple juice	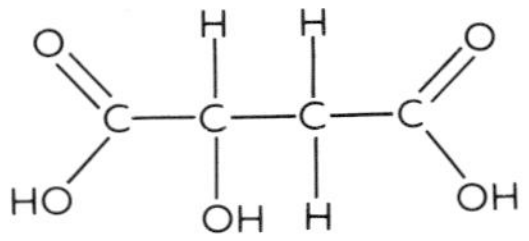
Oxalic acid	In rhubarb (mainly in leaves)	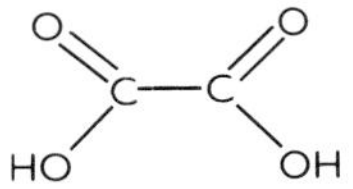

Table 7

Weak inorganic acids which you may have come across earlier are derived from carbon dioxide and sulphur dioxide on solution in water.

$$CO_2(g) + H_2O(l) \rightleftharpoons \underset{\text{carbonic acid}}{H_2CO_3(aq)} \rightleftharpoons \underset{\substack{\text{bicarbonate or}\\\text{hydrogencarbonate}\\\text{ion}}}{H^+(aq) + HCO_3^-(aq)} \rightleftharpoons \underset{\substack{\text{carbonate}\\\text{ion}}}{2H^+(aq) + CO_3^{2-}(aq)}$$

$$SO_2(g) + H_2O(l) \rightleftharpoons \underset{\substack{\text{sulphurous}\\\text{acid}}}{H_2SO_3(aq)} \rightleftharpoons \underset{\substack{\text{hydrogen-}\\\text{sulphite}\\\text{ion}}}{H^+(aq) + HSO_3^-(aq)} \rightleftharpoons \underset{\substack{\text{sulphite}\\\text{ion}}}{2H^+(aq) + SO_3^{2-}(aq)}$$

Carbonic acid is present in all rainfall and is responsible for the erosion of limestone on which it falls. This gives 'hard water', which is a solution of calcium hydrogencarbonate.

Sulphurous acid is one the major compounds present in 'acid rain' and is rather stronger than carbonic acid, although fortunately weaker than sulphuric acid. It is strong enough to accelerate metal corrosion and to erode limestone much faster than carbonic acid.

Ammonia forms a weakly alkaline solution known sometimes as ammonium hydroxide.

The alkalinity of the solution results from a reaction between ammonia and water molecules as in figure 9.

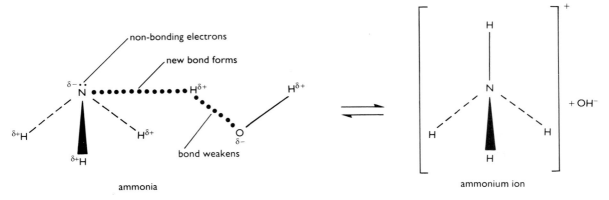

Figure 9

$$\text{or } NH_3(aq) + H_2O(l) \rightleftharpoons NH_4^+(aq) + OH^-(aq)$$

Compounds related to ammonia are the amines with the structural group:

An example is aminoethane or ethylamine, with the following structure:

They can ionise in solution by a mechanism similar to that of ammonia,

e.g. $C_2H_5NH_2(aq) + H_2O(l) \rightleftharpoons C_2H_5NH_3^+(aq) + OH^-(aq)$

The solution is slightly more alkaline than that of ammonia.

pH OF SALT SOLUTIONS

It is normally assumed that since salts can be made by neutralisation of an acid by an alkali the pH will be 'neutral' i.e. 7. In fact, the measured pH of salts is often not 7.

In general terms, in solution:

Salts of strong acid and strong alkali have pH 7

Salts of strong acid and weak alkali have pH < 7

Salts of strong alkali and weak acid have pH > 7

For example:

Sodium chloride and potassium nitrate are made from strong acids HCl and HNO_3 and strong alkalis NaOH and KOH. They have pH 7 in solution.

Ammonium chloride is made from the strong acid HCl and the weak alkali NH_3 and has a pH of about 5 in solution.

Sodium ethanoate is made from the strong alkali NaOH and the weak acid CH_3COOH and has a pH about 9 in solution.

The last two results can be explained as follows.

Sodium ethanoate in water

Ions present initially:

$Na^+ + CH_3COO^-$ from the salt (fully ionised)
$H^+ + OH^-$ from the water (a few only)

In the solution the CH_3COO^- and H^+ ions' concentrations exceed those normally found in the weak acid CH_3COOH, and the ions combine.

$$CH_3COO^-(aq) + H^+(aq) \rightarrow CH_3COOH(aq)$$

Removal of H^+ ions causes the water equilibrium to be disturbed.
$$H_2O(l) \rightarrow H^+(aq) + OH^-(aq)$$

Excess OH^- ions are formed, and the solution has pH greater than 7.

Similar considerations apply to sodium and potassium salts of other carboxylic acids and of carbonic and sulphurous acids.

Ammonium chloride in water

Ions present initially:

$NH_4^+ + Cl^-$ from the salt (fully ionised)
$H^+ + OH^-$ from the water (a few only)

> In the solution the NH_4^+ and OH^- ions' concentrations exceed those normally found in the weak alkali ammonia solution, and the ions form undissociated ammonia.
>
> $$NH_4^+(aq) + OH^-(aq) \rightarrow NH_3(aq) + H_2O(l)$$
>
> Removal of OH^- ions causes the water equilibrium to move to the right.
>
> $$H_2O(l) \rightarrow H^+(aq) + OH^-(aq)$$
>
> Excess H^+ ions are formed and the solution has pH less than 7.
> Similar explanations apply to the chlorides, sulphates and nitrates of NH_4^+ and of metals not in Groups I and II of the Periodic Table.

Examples for practice

1. When chlorine is dissolved in water the following equilibrium is set up.

$$Cl_2 + H_2O \rightleftharpoons 2H^+ + ClO^- + Cl^-$$

The hypochlorite ion, ClO^-, is responsible for the bleaching action of this solution. What effect on the bleaching efficiency of a solution of chlorine in water would the following have?
(a) Adding dilute nitric acid. (1)
(b) Adding sodium chloride crystals. (1)
(c) Adding potassium hydroxide solution. (1)
[PS](Total: 3)

2. Reaction (1): $H_2(g) + I_2(g) \rightleftharpoons 2HI(g)$
Reaction (2): $2CO(g) + O_2(g) \rightleftharpoons 2CO_2(g)$
Reaction (3): $CH_3OH(g) \rightleftharpoons CO(g) + 2H_2(g)$
(a) In which of the above reactions will an increase in pressure:
   (i) shift the position of equilibrium to the right, (1)
   (ii) have no effect on the equilibrium position. (1)
(b) In reaction (1), the forward reaction is exothermic. What effect, if any, will an increase in temperature have on the equilibrium position? (1)
(Total: 3)

3. (a) What is the pH of 0.01 mol I^{-1} solution of hydrochloric acid? (1)
(b) What assumption about the acid is made in calculating the pH value in (a)? (1)
(c) Estimate the pH value of a 0.005 mol I^{-1} solution of hydrochloric acid. (1)
(d) The pH of a solution of ethanoic acid is 3.5. Estimate the concentration of $H^+(aq)$ ions in the solution. (2)
(e) What would happen to the pH of the ethanoic acid solution if solid sodium ethanoate were added? Explain your answer. [PS](3)
(Total: 8)

4. Maleic acid is a weak acid. Its structural formula is shown below.

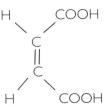

(a) How many moles of sodium hydroxide would be required to neutralise completely one mole of maleic acid? (1)

(b) Suggest a pH value for the salt sodium maleate. (1)

(c) What would you expect to happen on addition of bromine water to a solution of maleic acid? (1)

(Total: 3)

5. A group of pupils compared the conductivity of a dilute solution of sodium hydroxide with the conductivity of a dilute solution of methanoic acid. The circuit used is shown.

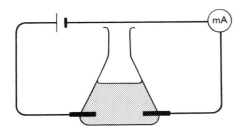

The circuit was used to measure the current passing through the solution. The pupils decided that the temperature had to be the same for both solutions.

(a) (i) State two more variables that would affect the current reading. [PS](2)

(ii) Explain how the experiment could be carried out in a fair way. [PS](1)

(b) (i) State whether a solution of the salt formed from the alkali and acid above is likely to be acidic, neutral or alkaline. (1)

(ii) Explain your answer. (2)

(SEB)(Total: 6)

6.

Acid	pH of 2 M aqueous solution
A CCl_3COOH	0.50
B $CHCl_2COOH$	0.90

(a) Which is the stronger acid? Explain your choice. (2)

(b) Acid A dissociates in water as follows:

$$CCl_3COOH(aq) \rightleftharpoons CCl_3COO^-(aq) + H^+(aq)$$

How would the equilibrium be affected by the addition of

(i) solid NaOH

(ii) solid NaCl

(iii) solid CH_3COONa? (3)

(c) Explain your answer in the case of solid CH_3COONa. (1)

(SEB)[PS](Total: 6)

7. Synthesis gas, a mixture of hydrogen and carbon monoxide, is prepared as shown below. Nickel is known to catalyse the reaction.

$$CH_4(g) + H_2O(g) \rightleftharpoons 3H_2(g) + CO(g)$$

(a) An increase in temperature increases the yield of synthesis gas. What information does this give about the enthalpy change in the forward reaction? (1)

(b) Using Le Chatelier's Principle explain how a change in pressure will affect the composition of the equilibrium mixture. (2)

(c) State how the rate of formation of synthesis gas will be affected by the use of the catalyst. (1)

(d) State how the composition of the equilibrium mixture will be affected by the use of the catalyst. (1)

(SEB)(Total: 5)

8. Solutions of the salt potassium cyanide (KCN) are alkaline.

(a) What is the formula of the acid from which potassium cyanide is derived? (1)

(b) Is it a strong or a weak acid? (1)

(c) Explain fully why potassium cyanide solution is alkaline. (3)

(SEB)(Total: 5)

8 Radioisotopes

Before commencing this section you should know and understand the following related information from the Standard Grade course.

(a) Atomic structure

Atoms consist of a nucleus and extranuclear electrons. The nucleus is made up of neutrons and protons. These particles are sometimes referred to as nucleons.

	Approximate mass	Charge	Location	Symbol
Proton	1	$+1$	nucleus	p or H
Neutron	1	0	nucleus	$^{1}_{0}n$
Electron	1/2000	-1	orbitals	$^{0}_{-1}e$

Table 1

Atomic number = number of protons (= number of electrons in an uncharged atom).

Mass number = number of protons + number of neutrons.

(b) Isotopes

(i) are different types of atoms of the same element, i.e. the same atomic number but different mass number, owing to different numbers of neutrons;
(ii) cannot be distinguished by chemical means, since chemical properties depend on electron arrangement;
(iii) can be represented by the nuclide notation, for example, $^{238}_{92}U$ represents the uranium (atomic number 92) isotope of mass number 238. For most purposes, the word 'nuclide' is interchangeable with 'isotope'.

CALCULATION OF RELATIVE ATOMIC MASS

From the values of percentage abundance and mass number of the isotopes of an element, the relative atomic mass can be calculated. It is the average value of the relative mass of all atoms of the element.

Relative atomic mass $=$
Σ(% abundance of each isotope $\times$ its mass number).

e.g. for silver of isotopic composition 51.4% $^{107}_{47}$Ag and 48.6% $^{109}_{47}$Ag:

$$\text{Relative atomic mass} \quad = \frac{51.4 \times 107}{100} + \frac{48.6 \times 109}{100}$$

$$= 54.998 \qquad + 52.974$$
$$= 107.972$$
$$= 108 \text{ to three significant figures.}$$

Example: Calculate the relative atomic mass of lead given the isotopic composition: 1.5% $^{204}_{82}$Pb, 23.6% $^{206}_{82}$Pb, 22.6% $^{207}_{82}$Pb, 52.3% $^{208}_{82}$Pb.

The set of values for lead may vary slightly from sample to sample, an unusual phenomenon for an element. The reason is that lead may be the end product of radioactive decay series, and different series produce different isotopes of lead.

All the values of mass used in this work are 'relative', that is they are comparisons with the mass of atoms of a specific isotope of carbon, $^{12}_{6}$C, which contains 6 protons and 6 neutrons per atom and is given an arbitary mass value of 12.000 atomic mass units. Other standards of mass have now been superceded.

DETERMINATION OF MASS NUMBERS AND ISOTOPE ABUNDANCES

The original function of the mass spectrometer was to determine the mass numbers of the various isotopes of the elements and the proportions of these isotopes in a normal sample of the element. It often provided the first concrete evidence of the existence of isotopes of an element.

The mass spectrometer is basically a means of causing atoms of an element to form positive ions by removing one or more electrons and then accelerating the ions to pass through a magnetic field of high intensity. Since the beam of ions moving at high speed resembles a current of positive electricity, it will experience a force tending to move it at right angles to the magnetic field and to its own direction of travel. It will follow a curved path in the magnetic field. The actual path will depend on the mass and the charge of the ion. The effect of a magnetic field on a beam of ions from an element made up of two isotopes is shown in figure 1.

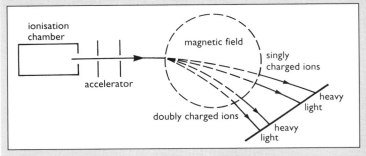

Figure 1   A simple mass spectrometer

A heavy isotope is deflected less than a lighter one, while a doubly charged ion is deflected more than a singly charged ion. For simplicity we chall only consider ions which have a single charge.

In practice, it is usually more convenient to place the detector at a particular point and vary the magnetic field so that the various beams pass across the detector in turn. The strength of field required to bring a stream of ions onto the detector is an indication of the mass: charge ratio of the ion. Once the magnetic field control has been calibrated, the mass: charge ratio of an ion responsible for a particular signal is given directly and the intensity of the signal is a measure of its proportion of the total. The read-out from the instrument can be given in graphical form as shown below.

The mass spectrometer read-outs can be used to calculate relative atomic mass as on page 157. For practice, calculate the relative atomic masses of magnesium and zinc from figure 2 and 3. (Note that in real mass spectrometer read-outs, there will be a repeated pattern of smaller peaks for the doubly charged ions e.g. for magnesium at 12, 12.5 and 13 mass/charge ratio. This repeated pattern is ignored in relative atomic mass calculations).

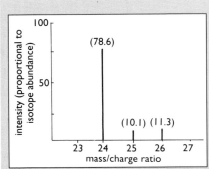

Figure 2   Mass spectrum of magnesium

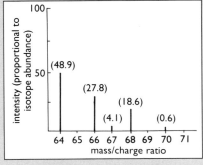

Figure 3   Mass spectrum of zinc

The mass spectrometer is nowadays used as a means of analysing alloys. The sample is vaporised and ionised by striking an arc between two pieces of the alloy used as electrodes. The instrument produces the composition in terms of isotopes of each element and their percentages.

The dating of rocks and archeological samples dealt with later in the chapter depends on the use of the mass spectrometer to determine the proportions of different isotopes.

RADIOACTIVITY

In 1896, Becquerel found that compounds of uranium emit an invisible radiation which will penetrate opaque materials and fog photographic plates. The phenomenon became known as radioactivity. Compounds of thorium behave in a similar fashion, as do natural isotopes of some other elements, and artificial isotopes of most elements.

The radiation was found to be affected by a magnetic or electrical field as shown in figure 4.

There are three types of radiation. Other experiments provide the information given in table 2.

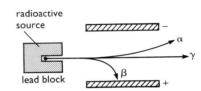

Figure 4 *Radiation deflected by an electric field between charged plates*

Name	Penetration	Nature	Symbol	Charge	Mass	
α (alpha)	few cm in air	He nucleus	$_2^4He$	2+	4	
β (beta)	thin metal foil	electron	$_{-1}^0e$	1−	1/2000	(approx.)
γ (gamma)	great thickness of concrete	EMR	none	none	none	

Table 2

Gamma radiation is non-particulate. It is electro-magnetic radiation, similar to X-radiation, but of a higher energy level. It is emitted alone or accompanying α or β radiation. The radiation is independent of the physical or chemical state of the element (i.e. independent of electronic arrangement) which indicates that it is connected solely with the nucleus.

Radioactivity is the result of unstable nuclei rearranging to form stable nuclei with the emission of energy. It can be shown that the mass of any atom is less than the sum of the masses of protons, neutrons and electrons of which it is composed. This 'mass defect' is equivalent to the 'binding energy' of the nucleus, mass and energy being related by the well known equation: $E = mc^2$.

The binding energy for heavy atoms is generally greater than that for light atoms, since more nucleons are being held together. However the binding energy per nucleon is not the same in all atoms. The most stable atoms have the greatest binding energy per nucleon. A graph of binding energy per nucleon of stable or near stable nuclides is shown in figure 5.

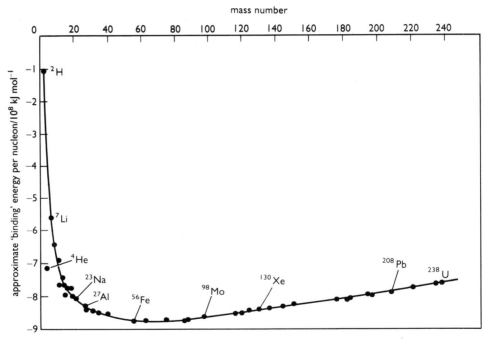

Figure 5 Binding energy per nucleon of stable or near stable nuclei

The distance from the curve up to the x-axis is a measure of the energy per nucleon required to dismantle the nucleus. If we consider the starting and finishing isotopes of one of the natural radioactive series, $^{238}_{92}U$ and $^{206}_{82}Pb$, we can see that more energy is required to dismantle the nucleus for the $^{206}_{82}Pb$ and it is therefore a more stable nucleus. In the change from $^{238}_{92}U$ to $^{206}_{82}Pb$ there is an emission of energy (possessed by the radiation and the kinetic energy of the various α and β particles emitted).

The stability of nuclei seems in some cases to be related to the neutron/proton balance. For small stable nuclei the numbers of neutrons and protons are approximately equal. Where a nucleus has too many neutrons it can become stable if a neutron changes into a proton and an electron, in other words a β particle, is projected from the nucleus.

$$\isotope[1][0]{n} \rightarrow \isotope[1][1]{p} + \isotope[0][-1]{e}$$

The neutron/proton ratio is reduced and a more stable nucleus may result. For example, carbon-14 emits β particles to form a stable isotope of nitrogen.

$$\isotope[14][6]{C} \rightarrow \isotope[14][7]{N} + \isotope[0][-1]{e}$$

Where isotopes with low atomic number have too few neutrons, electron capture may take place. An electron is removed from the first electron layer to combine with a proton to form a neutron. The electrons rearrange to refill the first layer.

$$\isotope[1][1]{p} + \isotope[0][-1]{e} \rightarrow \isotope[1][0]{n}$$

For example, argon-37 undergoes electron capture to form an isotope of chlorine.

$$\isotope[37][18]{Ar} + \isotope[0][-1]{e} \rightarrow \isotope[37][17]{Cl}$$

Beyond atomic number 83, almost all isotopes are unstable. They gain stability if they decrease in mass, see figure 5. Emission of α particles from the nucleus reduces the mass.

CHEMICAL EFFECT OF RADIOACTIVE DISINTEGRATIONS

The radiation originates in the nucleus, therefore the loss of α or β particles changes it considerably.

Loss of an α particle $\isotope[4][2]{He}$

This is equivalent to losing two protons (decreasing the atomic number by two) and two neutrons (overall decrease of mass number by four).

For example: $\isotope[232][90]{Th} \rightarrow \isotope[228][88]{Ra} + \isotope[4][2]{He}$

The total mass number (superscript) must be the

same on each side of the equation, as must be the total atomic number (subscript). NB: Since the atomic number of the product is 88, it is now radium.

Similarly: $$^{220}_{86}Rn \rightarrow {}^{216}_{84}Po + {}^{4}_{2}He$$

Loss of a β Particle

A β particle is an electron. Since the nucleus does not contain electrons, it is believed to be formed by:

$$\underset{\text{neutron}}{{}^{1}_{0}n} \rightarrow \underset{\text{proton}}{{}^{1}_{1}p} + \underset{\text{electron}}{{}^{0}_{-1}e}$$

Hence loss of the electron results in a gain of one unit of atomic number (one proton) without any change in mass number (since the mass of the proton is almost the same as the mass of the neutron).

For example: $$^{228}_{88}Ra \rightarrow {}^{228}_{89}Ac + {}^{0}_{-1}e$$

Again, total atomic number and mass number must be the same on each side of the equation. Since the product has atomic number 89 it is now actinium.

Similarly: $$^{216}_{84}Po \rightarrow {}^{216}_{85}At + {}^{0}_{-1}e$$

In fact the various 'daughter nuclei' are usually radioactive themselves, so that a whole series of radioactive disintegrations occurs until a stable isotope is reached, frequently an isotope of lead.

Artificial radioactivity

Many artificially produced radioactive isotopes are known. These can be made by bombarding stable isotopes with neutrons in a nuclear reactor. Since neutrons have no charge, they are not repelled by the positive nucleus.

For example: $$^{27}_{13}Al + {}^{1}_{0}n \rightarrow {}^{24}_{11}Na + {}^{4}_{2}He$$

The sodium isotope produced then decays by β emission: $^{24}_{11}Na \rightarrow {}^{24}_{12}Mg + {}^{0}_{-1}e$

Similarly: $^{32}_{16}S + {}^{1}_{0}n \rightarrow {}^{32}_{15}P + {}^{1}_{1}p$ (a proton). The phosphorus isotope produced is a β emitter: $^{32}_{15}P \rightarrow {}^{32}_{16}S + {}^{0}_{-1}e$

The 'target' material for the neutrons is usually a compound including the starting isotope. The other part of the compound may also be affected by the neutrons, so selection of the compound is a specialist task.

'PREDICTABILITY' OF RADIOACTIVE DECAY

The disintegration of any individual nucleus is a purely random event, and as already stated, is independent of chemical and physical factors. However, for a large enough population of unstable atoms, it is possible to calculate accurately how much of a radioisotope will be left after a given time.

Half-life

Radioactive decay of atoms of an isotope is such that the activity of the isotope decreases by half in a fixed time called the half-life of the isotope. Figure 6 shows the change of activity for an isotope with a half-life of 2 days.

Half-lives vary from seconds to millions of years and are characteristic of particular isotopes.

The half-life of any isotope is independent of the mass of the sample being investigated. It is independent of temperature, pressure, concentration, presence of catalysts or chemical state of the isotope. In the half-life, half of the atoms of the isotope decay but it is stressed the process is completely random and it is not possible to predict the time of decay of any individual atom. Half-life is often abbreviated to $t_{\frac{1}{2}}$.

After 'n' half-lives, the fraction of the original activity which remains is given by $(\frac{1}{2})^n$.

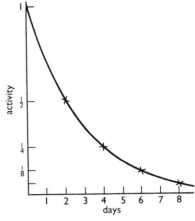

Figure 6 Change in activity with time for an isotope of half-life 2 days

Worked example 8.1

What fraction of the activity of a sample of $^{106}_{45}Rh$ will remain after three minutes? ($t_{\frac{1}{2}} = 30$ seconds)

$$t_{\frac{1}{2}} = 30 \text{ seconds, so 3 minutes} = 6t_{\frac{1}{2}}$$

Fraction of activity remaining $= (\frac{1}{2})^n = (\frac{1}{2})^6 = 1/64$

Worked example 8.2

The activity of a sample of $^{131}_{53}I$ is found to be only 1/16 of the activity when it arrived at a hospital 32 days earlier. What is the half-life of $^{131}_{53}I$?

$$\text{Fraction of activity remaining} = 1/16 = \left(\tfrac{1}{2}\right)^4$$

i.e. the sample has disintegrated through four half-lives in 32 days, therefore its half-life is 8 days.

THE USES OF RADIOISOTOPES

This is an ever expanding field, and so only certain important representative examples are given in the following sections.

Medical uses of radioisotopes

Radioactive isotopes have been used for a considerable time for the treatment of various types of cancer. For example the γ emitter $^{60}_{27}Co$ is used for the treatment of deep-seated tumours. The less penetrating β emitter $^{32}_{15}P$ is used for treating skin cancer by direct application to the affected area.

Radioactive isotopes can be used to monitor processes occurring in the body. An example is the use of radioactive iodine to investigate possible disease of the thyroid gland. The gland is scanned and a plot of concentration made. Diseased areas can be identified. To reduce overall exposure, short half-life $^{132}_{53}I$ and $^{123}_{53}I$ are now used instead of $^{131}_{53}I$.

Industrial applications of radioisotopes

A source of very penetrating radiation ($^{60}_{27}Co$ or $^{192}_{77}Ir$ are commonly used) is used to examine castings and welds for imperfections. A photographic film can be used as the detector, as in X-ray work.

Flow patterns in estuaries, leaks in pipelines and ventilation flows can be investigated using small quantities of short half-life isotopes which have negligible residual activity.

Radiosotopes can also be used to make routine measurements. Continuous monitoring of thickness of sheet material such as paper, plastic and thin metal sheet can be carried out using β sources, or γ sources for thicker metal sheet. Two identical sources can be used. The radiation from one passes through reference material of the required thickness, the radiation from the other passes through the material under test. If its thickness is correct, the detectors register the same signal. If the thickness varies, the signals differ and this difference can be used automatically to correct the fault.

Energy production

By far the most important method of obtaining energy from nuclear sources is nuclear fission. The basis of the method is the possibility of splitting some nuclei by bombarding them with slow-moving neutrons. The smaller nuclei produced are of elements in the centre of the periodic table. For example, one such change is:

$$^{235}_{92}U + ^{1}_{0}n \rightarrow ^{236}_{92}U \rightarrow ^{140}_{54}Xe + ^{94}_{38}Sr + 2^{1}_{0}n$$

Figure 5 shows that the two new nuclei have a lower energy level than the original nucleus and the energy liberated is available for use in generating electricity. However it is important to note that more neutrons are set free than are used, as shown in the above equation. This means that the reaction becomes a self-sustaining chain reaction, although in practice this only occurs if more than a certain 'critical mass' of $^{235}_{92}U$ is used. Figure 7 illustrates the fission of a $^{235}_{92}U$ nucleus.

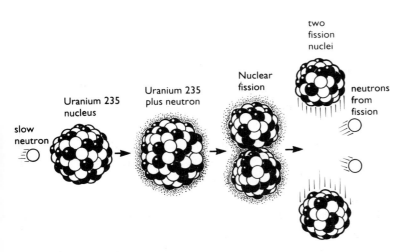

two
fission
nuclei

Nuclear
fission

neutrons
from
fission

Uranium 235
plus neutron

Uranium 235
nucleus

slow
neutron

Figure 7 Uranium fission

A calculation based on the equation above shows that fission of one mole, 235 g, of $^{235}_{92}U$ yields about 19×10^6 MJ of energy. The combustion of carbon to produce the same amount of energy would need at least 60 tonnes of high quality coal and would produce some 220 tonnes of CO_2 in the atmosphere.

There are obvious advantages in the use of nuclear power in electricity generation. No CO_2 is contributed to the atmosphere to worsen the 'greenhouse effect', there is no contribution to 'acid rain' and the routine risk of death or injury to workers in the nuclear industry is far lower than that of coal miners. Major disadvantages are the potentially catastrophic consequences of a serious accident at a nuclear plant, although of very low probability, the difficulties of disposing of the waste fission products and the environmental damage from uranium mining. This is not the place to enter the pro- and anti-nuclear debate but it is worth commenting that more emotion than reason is often in evidence from some of the participants. At present Scotland obtains 50% of its electricity from nuclear sources.

$^{235}_{92}U$ is only a small proportion of natural uranium (0.7%). The majority is the non-fissionable $^{238}_{92}U$. The elderly British 'Magnox' reactors operate using natural uranium, the modern AGR (advanced gas-cooled reactor) uses uranium enriched with $^{235}_{92}U$ to 2.3% and the PWR (pressurised water reactor) uses enriched uranium to 3.2% $^{235}_{92}U$. The $^{238}_{92}U$ is not discarded however, It 'captures' neutrons to produce $^{239}_{94}Pu$.

$$^{238}_{92}U + ^{1}_{0}n \rightarrow {}^{239}_{92}U \rightarrow {}^{239}_{93}Np + {}^{0}_{-1}e$$

$$^{239}_{93}Np \rightarrow {}^{239}_{94}Pu + {}^{0}_{-1}e \qquad t_{\frac{1}{2}} \ 2.33 \ days$$

Plutonium, Pu, is itself fissionable and can be used in other reactors to produce energy.

One British reactor type is shown in figure 8. The Torness reactor is an Advanced Gas-cooled Reactor.

The possibility of exhausting supplies of $^{235}_{92}U$, but more importantly the problem of disposing of fission products, has led to much research into energy production from nuclear fusion. Another look at figure 5 will show that some of the very light nuclei can form heavier nuclei with the production of even more energy than fission generates. One such reaction under study is: $^2_1H + ^3_1H \rightarrow {}^4_2He + {}^1_1H$

A 1000 MW power station would, it is claimed, require only one ton of fuel per year.

Another possible reaction, although this would require lithium rather than the more common hydrogen isotopes, is:

$$^6_3Li + {}^1_0n \rightarrow {}^3_1H + {}^4_2He$$

This produces more energy than the previous reaction. Furthermore, the tritium produced could be used in bringing about the first reaction. It is in fact possible to devise several reactions which would form a 'chain', but the major difficulty is in bringing the nuclei together (against their electrostatic repulsion), for a long enough period for fusion to take place. Various very expensive, and so far unsuccessful, devices are being tested, such as the one at Culham in England for a European consortium. In early 1989 the possibility of 'cold fusion' by electrolysis raised great hopes because of its simplicity. These hopes were dashed.

Author's note: In November 1991, the 'Jet' team at Culham announced the first successful demonstration of a controlled fusion reaction, albeit for only a few seconds.

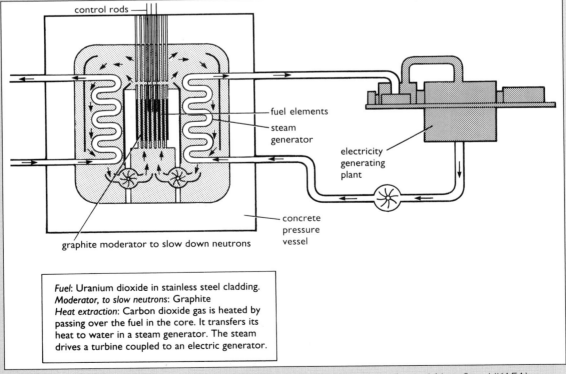

control rods

fuel elements

steam generator

electricity generating plant

graphite moderator to slow down neutrons

concrete pressure vessel

Fuel: Uranium dioxide in stainless steel cladding.
Moderator, to slow neutrons: Graphite
Heat extraction: Carbon dioxide gas is heated by passing over the fuel in the core. It transfers its heat to water in a steam generator. The steam drives a turbine coupled to an electric generator.

Figure 8 Advanced Gas-Cooled Reactor (AGR), Thermal Reactor – graphite moderated (data from UKAEA)

Agricultural uses

Tracer techniques are widely used in agriculture. One example is the use of $^{32}_{15}P$ in phosphate fertilisers to observe the use of phosphate by the growing plant. Another example is to use CO_2 labelled with $^{14}_6C$ to follow the way in which carbon is incorporated successfully into different plant constituents following photosynthesis.

More controversial is the use of γ irradiation of food crops to kill bacteria and moulds and increase storage life. The method is not popular in the UK, but in other European countries it is already widely used. It should be emphasised that there is no residual radiation from the source left on the crop.

Dating

Radioactive isotopes are constantly decaying at a known rate so the age of materials containing them can be estimated by finding the present activity of the isotope.

For example $^{14}_6C$ is used to date archeological specimens between about 600 and 10 000 years old. The method depends on the production of $^{14}_6C$ in the atmosphere by bombardment of nitrogen with neutrons formed from the effects of cosmic rays on other atoms.

$$^{14}_7N + ^1_0n \rightarrow {}^{14}_6C + {}^1_1p$$

This $^{14}_6C$, like $^{12}_6C$, is constantly taken up by growing plants then by animals, so that their $^{14}_6C : {}^{12}_6C$ ratio is known. When they die however, the $^{14}_6C$ decays:

$$^{14}_6C \rightarrow {}^{14}_7N + {}^{\,0}_{-1}e \quad (t_{\frac{1}{2}} = 5\,600\,\text{years})$$

By measuring the $^{14}_6C : {}^{12}_6C$ ratio the time since the sample 'died' can be estimated.

There are several systems which use long half-life isotopes to date rocks, but for checking the age of vintage wines the short half-life tritium, ^3_1H, has often been used ($t_{\frac{1}{2}} = 12.4$ years). Worked example 8.3 illustrates this use of tritium.

Worked example 8.3

A sample of wine shows a β emission rate from tritium ^3_1H which is 1/8 of that from wine bottled at the present day. If the half-life of tritium is 12.4 years, and its concentration in the atmosphere and in water exposed to the atmosphere is assumed to have remained constant, for how many years has the wine been bottled?

Activity remaining is 1/8 of original β activity. i.e. $\left(\frac{1}{2}\right)^3$

Therefore three half-lives have elapsed = 3 × 12.4 years.
The wine is approximately 37 years old.

BACKGROUND RADIATION

Everyone is exposed to radiation from various sources at all times. This radiation is background radiation. In addition most of us are exposed to other sources for medical reasons and some of us because of our occupations. More controversial is the exposure of all of us to radiation from leakages from nuclear plants and disposal of radioactive waste. The numbers in figure 9 show the relative magnitudes of these radiation sources. The average individual dose to a person in the UK is about 2 millisievert per year, 90% being from natural sources. Any member of the public is only allowed to receive 1 mSv year after year from human activity (excluding medical exposure). 2mSv per year gives a risk equivalent to smoking 20 cigarettes per year.

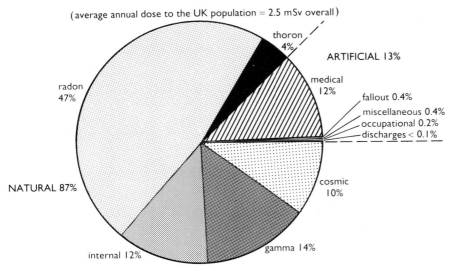

(average annual dose to the UK population = 2.5 mSv overall)

Figure 9 Sources of radiation affecting the UK population (1988 figures)

Much of the radon shown in figure 9 as a source of radiation is produced in igneous rocks which contain radioisotopes. It then escapes to the atmosphere. Houses in Aberdeen which are built of granite can have higher than average concentrations of radiation in their atmospheres.

Examples for practice

1. Write down the symbol of the particle formed when
(i) a francium atom loses its outer electron
(ii) $^{223}_{87}Fr$ loses a beta particle. (2)

2. Complete the following equations:

(a) $^{234}_{90}Th \rightarrow + ^{0}_{-1}e$
(b) $^{222}_{86}Rn \rightarrow + ^{4}_{2}He$ (2)

3. Find x, y and z in the following equations:

$^{6}_{3}Li + ^{1}_{0}n \rightarrow ^{3}_{1}H + x$

$^{234}_{92}U \rightarrow y + ^{4}_{2}He$

$z \rightarrow ^{212}_{83}Bi + ^{0}_{-1}e$ (3)

4. Polonium-210 is radioactive, emitting alpha (α) particles. Calculate the number of alpha particles emitted by 1 g of polonium-210 in a time equal to two half-lives. [PS](3)

5. The isotope $^{131}_{53}I$ is radioactive and is manufactured, for medicinal use, by the neutron bombardment of $^{127}_{53}I$.

$^{127}_{53}I + 4^{1}_{0}n \rightarrow ^{131}_{53}I$

(a) Calculate the number of neutrons required to produce 1 mole of radioactive iodine molecules. [PS](2)
(b) If, 24 days after manufacture, only 32.75 g of the original mole of radioactive iodine remains, calculate the half-life of the isotope $^{131}_{53}I$. (2)
(SEB)(Total: 4)

6. (a) The radioactive isotope $^{221}_{87}Fr$ decays to form a stable isotope $^{b}_{a}X$ by the following sequence of emissions:

$$\alpha, \alpha, \beta, \alpha, \beta$$

Identify element X and write values for 'a' and 'b'. (2)
(b)

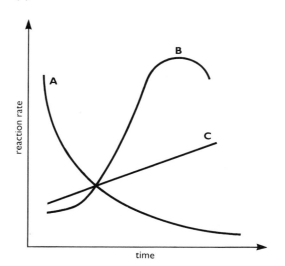

During fission of uranium, one of the reactions which occurs is:

$$^{235}_{92}U + ^{1}_{0}n \rightarrow ^{144}_{56}Ba + ^{99}_{36}Kr + 2^{1}_{0}n$$

(i) Which of the above curves could represent this reaction?
(ii) Explain your choice. [PS](2)
(SEB)(Total: 4)

7. (a) Part of a radioactive decay series is shown below.

$$^{231}_{90}Th \xrightarrow{-\beta} \text{isotope } X \rightarrow \text{isotope } Y \xrightarrow{-\beta} {}^{227}_{90}Th$$

(i) Identify isotopes X and Y. (2)

(ii) Which type of decay occurs between isotope X and isotope Y? (1)

(b) The radioactive isotope $^{210}_{84}Po$ decays to $^{206}_{82}Pb$, which is stable. Calculate the mass of lead which would be formed from 1 mole of $^{210}_{84}Po$ after two half-lives. [PS](2)

(SEB)(Total: 5)

8. (a) One of the compounds present in the gas mixture obtained by cracking naphtha contains 82.75% carbon and 17.25% hydrogen. Calculate the empirical formula for the compound. (1)

(b) In a mass spectrometer particles are affected in various ways. Some complete molecules lose an electron to form an ion. In addition this ion can break up into smaller fragments, some of which are ions. In this way the mass spectrum of a single compound often shows a large number of ions of different masses which may represent single atoms, fragments made up of several atoms, or complete molecules. For example CH_3^+ is a typical fragment.

A mass spectrum of the compound described in (a) gives the following result.

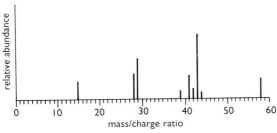

(i) Use this information and the empirical formula from (a) to work out the molecular formula for the compound. [PS](2)

(ii) Which fragment of this molecule could

have given the peak at the mass/charge ratio of 29? [PS](1)

(SEB)(Total: 4)

9. The mass spectrum of sulphur dioxide, shown below, supports the idea that molecules become fragmented when ionised in a mass spectrometer.

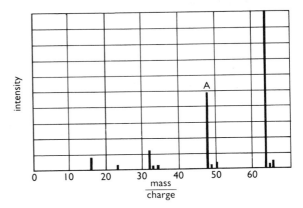

The sample of sulphur dioxide used contained only one isotope of oxygen, ($^{16}_8O$).

(a) How many isotopes of sulphur did the sample contain? (1)

(b) Write the formula for the ion responsible for the group of peaks at A. (1)

(SEB)[PS](Total: 2)

10. (a) A radioisotope X decays to a stable product as shown in the following graph.

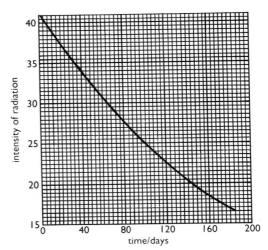

(i) Determine the half-life of X. [PS](1)

(ii) Identify X. (Use the Data Booklet, page 8.) [PS](1)

(iii) Write a nuclear equation for the decay of X. [PS](1)

(b) The mass spectrometer is used to determine mass numbers.

(i) Which type of particle moves through a mass spectrometer? (1)

(ii) Explain the significance of the word relative in the term 'relative atomic mass'. (1)

(iii) Neon has two isotopes ^{20}Ne and ^{x}Ne. If the relative atomic mass of neon is 20.2 and the abundance of ^{20}Ne is 90% calculate the mass number, x, of the second isotope. (**Working must be shown**). [PS](2)

(c) Many radioisotopes are made by bombarding stable atoms with alpha particles, neutrons or protons.

(i) Explain why neutrons are widely used for producing radioisotopes. [PS](1)

(ii) Why are beta particles not used to produce radioisotopes? [PS](1)

(iii) Explain how radioactivity can be used to estimate the age of organic remains. (3)

(SEB)(Total: 12)

PERIODIC TABLE OF ELEMENTS

KEY:
Relative Atomic Mass
Symbol
Name
Atomic Number

TRANSITION ELEMENTS

1 **H** Hydrogen 1																	4 **He** Helium 2
7 **Li** Lithium 3	9 **Be** Beryllium 4											11 **B** Boron 5	12 **C** Carbon 6	14 **N** Nitrogen 7	16 **O** Oxygen 8	19 **F** Fluorine 9	20 **Ne** Neon 10
23 **Na** Sodium 11	24 **Mg** Magnesium 12											27 **Al** Aluminium 13	28 **Si** Silicon 14	31 **P** Phosphorus 15	32 **S** Sulphur 16	35.5 **Cl** Chlorine 17	40 **Ar** Argon 18
39 **K** Potassium 19	40 **Ca** Calcium 20	45 **Sc** Scandium 21	48 **Ti** Titanium 22	51 **V** Vanadium 23	52 **Cr** Chromium 24	55 **Mn** Manganese 25	56 **Fe** Iron 26	59 **Co** Cobalt 27	59 **Ni** Nickel 28	64 **Cu** Copper 29	65 **Zn** Zinc 30	70 **Ga** Gallium 31	73 **Ge** Germanium 32	75 **As** Arsenic 33	79 **Se** Selenium 34	80 **Br** Bromine 35	84 **Kr** Krypton 36
85.5 **Rb** Rubidium 37	88 **Sr** Strontium 38	89 **Y** Yttrium 39	91 **Zr** Zirconium 40	93 **Nb** Niobium 41	96 **Mo** Molybdenum 42	**Tc** Technetium 43	101 **Ru** Ruthenium 44	103 **Rh** Rhodium 45	106 **Pd** Palladium 46	108 **Ag** Silver 47	112 **Cd** Cadmium 48	115 **In** Indium 49	119 **Sn** Tin 50	122 **Sb** Antimony 51	128 **Te** Tellurium 52	127 **I** Iodine 53	131 **Xe** Xenon 54
133 **Cs** Caesium 55	137 **Ba** Barium 56	139 **La** Lanthanum 57	178.5 **Hf** Hafnium 72	181 **Ta** Tantalum 73	184 **W** Tungsten 74	186 **Re** Rhenium 75	190 **Os** Osmium 76	192 **Ir** Iridium 77	195 **Pt** Platinum 78	197 **Au** Gold 79	201 **Hg** Mercury 80	204 **Tl** Thallium 81	207 **Pb** Lead 82	209 **Bi** Bismuth 83	**Po** Polonium 84	**At** Astatine 85	**Rn** Radon 86
Fr Francium 87	**Ra** Radium 88	**Ac** Actinium 89															

LANTHANIDES

139 **La** Lanthanum 57	140 **Ce** Cerium 58	141 **Pr** Praseodymium 59	144 **Nd** Neodymium 60	**Pm** Promethium 61	150 **Sm** Samarium 62	152 **Eu** Europium 63	157 **Gd** Gadolinium 64	159 **Tb** Terbium 65	162.5 **Dy** Dysprosium 66	165 **Ho** Holmium 67	167 **Er** Erbium 68	169 **Tm** Thulium 69	173 **Yb** Ytterbium 70	175 **Lu** Lutetium 71

ACTINIDES

Ac Actinium 89	232 **Th** Thorium 90	**Pa** Protactinium 91	238 **U** Uranium 92	**Np** Neptunium 93	**Pu** Plutonium 94	**Am** Americium 95	**Cm** Curium 96	**Bk** Berkelium 97	**Cf** Californium 98	**Es** Einsteinium 99	**Fm** Fermium 100	**Md** Mendelevium 101	**No** Nobelium 102	**Lw** Lawrencium 103

NB: Relative atomic masses are shown only for elements which have stable isotopes or isotopes with very long half-life.

ANSWERS: TO NUMERICAL EXAMPLES

UNIT I

4(a) 190 kJ   (b) 20 kJ.
6(a) (i) 5 s   (b) (i) 14°C.

UNIT 3: SECTION A

1(a) 2   (b) 0.25   (c) 0.1   (d) 8.
2(a) 52.2%   (b) 42.1%   (c) 10.0%   (d) 15.4%.
3(a) CH_2 (b) Na_2SO_3 (c) PbN_2O_6 (d) CH_2O.
Molecular formulae: A C_3H_6, D $C_6H_{12}O_6$.
4(a) (i) 0.02   (ii) 3.4 g.
(b) (i) 6   (ii) 636 g.
(c) (i) 0.5   (ii) 74 g.
(d) (i) 2.5   (ii) 330 g.
5(a) $0.5 \, mol \, l^{-1}$ (b) $2.5 \, mol \, l^{-1}$ (c) $0.05 \, mol \, l^{-1}$ (d) $5 \, mol \, l^{-1}$.
6(a) 8 g   (b) 20 kg   (c) 5.55 g.
7(a) $2.5 \, mol \, l^{-1}$ (b) $0.5 \, mol \, l^{-1}$ (c) $0.3 \, mol \, l^{-1}$.
8(i) $1.82 \, mol \, 1^{-1}$ (ii) $0.80 \, mol \, l^{-1}$.

UNIT 3: SECTION B

1 4.03 g.
2 1.12 g.
3 8 g.
4 2 A.
5(b) Cu^{2+}.
6(a) Fort William: (i) 1410 kg   (ii) 112 800 kg.
       Kinlochleven: (i) 322 kg   (ii) 32 200 kg.
(b) 77.8%   (c) 107.4 kg.

UNIT 3: SECTION C

1(a) 1.81×10^{24} (b) 3.01×10^{23} (c) 6.11×10^{24}.
2 6.02×10^{25}.
3 (a) (i) 3.01×10^{23} (ii) 6.02×10^{23}.
(b) (i) 6.02×10^{24} (ii) 1.81×10^{25}.
(c) (i) 6.02×10^{22} (ii) 3.01×10^{23}.
(d) (i) 6.02×10^{21} (ii) 2.71×10^{23}.
4 24.5 g.
5(a) (i) 1.81×10^{24} (ii) 1.81×10^{24}.
(b) (i) 1.20×10^{23} (ii) 6.02×10^{22}.
(c) (i) 1.51×10^{23} (ii) 3.01×10^{23}.
(d) (i) 3.01×10^{23} (ii) 4.52×10^{23}.

6 0.1.
7 9.3 g.
8 (a) 1.20×10^{24} (b) 2.41×10^{23}
9 8.43×10^{23}.
10 2.01×10^{24}.

UNIT 3: SECTION D

1(a) 0.833 g l^{-1} (b) 0.708 g l^{-1} (c) 1.75 g l^{-1}.
2(a) N_2: 22.3 l, CO_2: 22.3 l   (b) 22.3 l.
3 $30 \text{ cm}^3 O_2$, $60 \text{ cm}^3 NO_2$.
4(a) C_4H_8.
5(b) $25 \text{ cm}^3 N_2$, $75 \text{ cm}^3 H_2$ (c) 25 cm^3.
6(a) (i) 400 cm^3 (ii) 200 cm^3.
  (b) (i) 6.5 l   (ii) 4 l.
  (c) (i) 45 cm^3 (ii) 30 cm^3.
7(a) $6 \text{ l } CO_2$ (b) $4.8 \text{ l } H_2$ (c) $2.4 \text{ l } H_2$.

UNIT 3: SECTION E

1 (a) $5 \text{ cm}^3 O_2$ excess, $10 \text{ cm}^3 CO_2$ produced.
  (b) $5 \text{ cm}^3 C_3H_8$ excess, $15 \text{ cm}^3 CO_2$ produced.
2(b) $95 \text{ cm}^3 O_2$ excess and $100 \text{ cm}^3 CO_2$ produced.
3 (a) (i) CuO   (ii) 8 g   (b) (i) HNO_3 (ii) 3.31 g.
  (c) (i) Al   (ii) 20.0 g.
4 $BaCl_2$ excess, 4.66 g $BaSO_4$.
5(c) 80 cm^3 (d) 110 cm^3.

UNIT 3: SECTION F

1(a) 95%   (b) 90%.
2 5 g.
3(i) 50%   (ii) 4.27 g   (iii) 35%.

UNIT 3: SECTION G

4 (a) 0.16 mol l^{-1}.
  (b) 0.8 mol l^{-1}.
  (c) 1 mol l^{-1}.
  (d) 0.1 mol l^{-1}.

UNIT 4

5(d) (ii) -122 kJmol^{-1}.
6(d) -5434 kJmol^{-1}.

UNIT 6

1 $-1346\ \text{kJ mol}^{-1}$.
2 $-878\ \text{kJ mol}^{-1}$.
3 $34.8\ \text{kJ mol}^{-1}$.
7(a) $327\ \text{kJ mol}^{-1}$ (b) $-107\ \text{kJ mol}^{-1}$.
8 $-50\ \text{kJ mol}^{-1}$.
9 $-96\ \text{kJ mol}^{-1}$.
10 $-44\ \text{kJ mol}^{-1}$.
12(b) $51\ \text{kJ mol}^{-1}$.
13(a) $53\ \text{kJ mol}^{-1}$.
14(b) $-335\ \text{kJ mol}^{-1}$.
16(b) $-716.5\ \text{kJ mol}^{-1}$.

UNIT 7

3(a) 2 (c) > 2 (i.e. 2.3) (d) $0.003\ \text{mol l}^{-1}$.
4(a) 2 (b) > 7.

UNIT 8

1(i) Fr^+ (ii) $^{223}_{88}\text{Ra}$.
2(a) $^{234}_{91}\text{Pa}$ (b) $^{218}_{84}\text{Po}$.
3 x: $^{4}_{2}\text{He}$, y: $^{230}_{90}\text{Th}$, z: $^{212}_{82}\text{Pb}$.
4 2.14×10^{21}.
5(a) 4.8×10^{24} (b) 8 days.
6(a) a : 83, b : 209.
7(a) (i) $^{231}_{91}\text{Pa}$, $^{227}_{89}\text{Ac}$ (ii) α (b) 154.5 g.
8(a) C_2H_5 (b) (i) C_4H_{10} (ii) $C_2H_5{}^+$.
9(a) 3 (b) SO^+.
10(a) (i) About 140 days (ii) $^{210}_{84}\text{Po}$ (iii) $^{210}_{84}\text{Po} \rightarrow {}^{4}_{2}\text{He} + {}^{206}_{82}\text{Pb}$.
   (b) (iii) 22.

INDEX

British Library Cataloguing in Publication Data
Allan, Eric
  Higher Grade Chemistry: essential facts and theory.
  – 2nd ed.
  I. Title   II. Harris, John
  540

ISBN 0 340 54918 1

First published 1991
Second Impression 1992

© 1991

Typeset by Taurus Graphics, Abingdon, Oxon.
Printed in Great Britain for the educational publishing division of Hodder & Stoughton Ltd, Mill Road, Dunton Green, Sevenoaks, Kent by Thomson Litho Ltd, East Kilbride.